THE NAUTICAL INSTITUTE

BRIDGE TEAM MANAGEMENT

A Practical Guide

Captain A. J. Swift, MNI

Senior Lecturer, Simulation Section,
Maritime Operations Centre, Warsash

Foreword by
Captain P. Boyle, FNI
President, The Nautical Institute

First published 1993 by The Nautical Institute
202 Lambeth Road, London SE1 7LQ, UK.
Telephone: 071-928 1351

Typeset and printed in England by Silverdale Press, Silverdale Road, Hayes, Middlesex UB3 3BH.

ISBN 1 870077 14 8

BRIDGE TEAM MANAGEMENT

CONTENTS

BACKGROUND

TEAM MANAGEMENT—Training and Coaching—Wellbeing—Morale

ERROR CHAINS—Indications—Ambiguity—Distraction—Inadequacy/
Confusion—Communications Breakdown—Improper Conn—
Non Compliance with Plan—Procedural Violation

CASUALTIES AND CAUSES—Lack of Double Watch—Insufficient
Personnel—Calling the Master—Lookouts—Manning the Wheel—
Autopilot Changeover—Reducing Speed

GROUNDINGS AND CAUSES—Planned Track—Track Monitoring
Track Regain—Double Check Fixing—Visual Fixing—Echo-Sounder—
Light Identification—Decision Corroboration

BRIDGE ORGANISATION—Individual Role

Information Sources—Ocean Passages—Coastal Passages

No-go Areas—Margins of Safety—Safe Water—Ocean Tracks—
Coastal Tracks—Chart Change—Distance Off

Deviation from Track

Underkeel Clearance—Tidal Window—Stream Allowance

Course Alteration—Wheel-Over

Parallel Indexing—ARPA Mapping—Waypoints

Abort—Contingencies

Position Fixing—Primary and Secondary Fixing—Conspicuous
Objects—Landfall Lights—Fix Frequency & Regularity

Additional Information—Reporting Points—Anchor Clearance—
Pilot Boarding—Tug Engagement—Traffic

SITUATIONAL AWARENESS—Transits—Compass Error—
Leading Lines—Clearing Marks—Clearing Bearings

RANGE OF LIGHTS—Geographical—Luminous—Nominal—
Landfall Lights—Extreme Range—Echo Sounder

INFORMATION—Overcrowding—Planning Book—Conning Notes

MASTERS APPROVAL—Plan Changes

TACTICS—ETA for Tide—ETA for Daylight—Traffic Conditions—
ETA at Destination—Tidal Stream & Current—Plan Modification

ADDITIONAL PERSONNEL—Briefing—Fatigue

PREPARATION—for Voyage—of Bridge

FIXING—Method—Visual Bearings—Frequency—Regularity—
EP—Soundings

CROSS-TRACK ERROR

TIME MANAGEMENT

LOOKOUT

OBSERVATION—Underkeel Clearance—Waypoints—Transits—
Leading Lines—Natural Leading Lines—Clearing Marks and Bearings—
Dipping Distances—Light Sectors

Single Watchkeeper—with Lookout—Helmsman—Master on Bridge—
Additional Officer

SCENARIO

Responsibilities—Planning—Information Exchange—Monitoring

THE BRIDGE OPERATIONS PROGRAMME

A message from The Secretary-General of the IMO

WHENEVER a ship puts to sea, the master and navigating officers have a duty both in public and commercial law to navigate competently at all times. Upon their actions depend the successful outcome of the voyage, safety at sea and protection of the marine environment.

The International Maritime Organization recognises the essential requirement that all watchkeeping officers must be properly trained. This training needs to be initiated ashore and before watchkeeping officers are qualified to take a navigational watch, they need to be proficient in such disciplines as navigation, the application of the rules to avoid collisions and seamanship. IMO has resolved to revise the STCW Convention through an accelerated process and together with the on-board training proposed in this programme will represent a major contribution to the improvement of standards that is so important.

It is, however, at sea on the bridge of ships that watchkeepers have to work together and make decisions. Once they have been trained, good practices need to be continually refreshed and that is why I am strongly supporting these measures by The Nautical Institute and Videotel Marine International to provide leadership, encouragement and positive advice through the *Bridge Operations Programme*.

Each part of the programme has been designed to re-enforce the application of practices and principles developed in IMO, industry codes and shipboard routines. The programme starts with the trainee, ends with the master whilst involving the pilot. In so doing, owners and managers are also reminded that they have obligations, too. They have to provide the means of keeping charts up to date, equipment functional and the standards of training appropriate to the responsibilities that watchkeeping entails.

Above all, this imaginative programme demonstrates the level of knowledge and skills applied in pursuit of safe ship operation. We come to appreciate that watchkeeping is very responsible work and that supporting the human element demands long term commitment, which is likely to be most effective if it provides a common sense of purpose amongst the bridge team.

Watchkeeping officers through their diligence and professionalism provide a highly valued service to society. This contribution is recognised by IMO and in launching this project, I wish to pay tribute to the world's seafarers and those organisations which are working with us to enhance safe ship operations.□

W. A. O'Neil

ACKNOWLEDGEMENTS

THIS BOOK has been developed to give meaning to the convention, standards and resolutions prepared by the International Maritime Organization and I wish to acknowledge the valuable work undertaken at the intergovernmental level to provide the essential international framework for bridge operational standards.

The principles of the International Chamber of Shipping *Bridge Procedures Guide* have been used as a basis for shipping company practice, whilst the texts and notices issued by the UK Department of Transport have provided essential guidance in the compilation of this volume.

Over the years, fleet managers and superintendents from companies all over the world have discussed their requirements and been instrumental in measuring performance from which we have been able to assess the effectiveness of the methods chosen.

A book like this cannot be conceived without the accumulated experience of over 3,000 officers attending training courses who have in their own way either directly or indirectly contributed to my understanding of bridge management. To all these people and organisations I owe particular thanks, for without their professional commitment this book is unlikely to have been written.

I also wish to thank my colleagues at the Simulation Section of the Maritime Operations Centre, Southampton Institute of Higher Education, Warsash, for their support in production of this book, with special thanks to Roy Stanbrook, MNI.□

FOREWORD

THE SAFE CONDUCT of a ship at sea is the principal discipline upon which the nautical profession is based. Yet surprisingly it is a subject which is not widely documented and upon which there are different opinions. This is strange because the navigation of a ship is an identifiable task whose outcome is the same in all cases. In spite of that there are many different styles of navigation practised at sea.

Central to this book on *Bridge Team Management* is the question 'Is there a need for a well defined bridge organisation?' The question cannot be answered until all elements of the system have been fully considered, and they are the ship, the equipment, the voyage itinerary, the officers, the crew and the Master, support by the company and the organisational structure in which decisions are taken.

It is too easy to focus on individual items of equipment, the character of the Master or the ability of the officers and to generalise about the performance of the system. It is also very difficult for any individual to have the complete overview or be able to influence an entire operation.

Increasingly there are discontinuities in management as ships are bought and sold, crews are changed, and new equipment fitted, whilst the training methods of different countries vary and multi-national crews have their own characteristics.

Trying to raise standards of bridge operations poses particular problems in this complex international industry where some owners elect to supply the minimum navigational outfit as specified in the Solas Convention whilst others seek to develop specialised navigational systems based upon the latest technology.

For these reasons I particularly welcome this book on *Bridge Team Management* because it focuses on the key subject of organisation, without which it is not possible to ensure consistent results. Now that the book has been written, we may wonder why it was not produced before, and part of the answer I suggest lies in the fact that traditional maritime nations developed their own response to navigational safety.

There are of course many acceptable ways of navigating but there has to be a firm basis and understanding of underlying principles before the international shipping can share a common purpose. The main purpose of good bridge team management is to ensure safe and timely arrival at a destination. A secondary purpose is to avoid the consequential loss than can occur if there is a collision or stranding. For this reason good bridge practice deserves the widest support from governments concerned with loss of life and protection of the marine environment.

Clearly, all industrial enterprise will benefit from sound loss prevention methods and in particular the insurance industry must see the advantage in adopting positive bridge management methods. The book codifies a wealth of experience and provides the platform to plan ahead, develop training and above all implement effective bridge organisation.☐

Captain Peter Boyle, FNI
President, The Nautical Institute

BACKGROUND TO THE MARITIME OPERATIONS CENTRE

SINCE 1985 the College of Maritime Studies, which had its origins as far back as 1850 initially as a University College School of Navigation in the early 20th century, is now part of the Southampton Institute of Higher Education. Established in Warsash just outside Southampton in 1946, the School of Navigation has changed through the decades to meet the changing needs of a national and international industry without losing sight of its mission: 'to provide the maritime and shipping industries with high quality training, consultancy and research services'.

Today, the Maritime Operations Centre continues to provide those services with highly experienced staff, most of whom have held command, and state of the art technology in the form of sophisticated ship's bridge, radar, VTS, machinery space and cargo-handling simulators. Bridge Team training, using ship's bridge simulators, has been conducted at Warsash since 1977 and Captain Swift has been a member of this team since 1980. In addition to Bridge Team Management training, ship-handling courses for pilots, masters and senior officers are conducted with the use of accurately scaled manned models operating on a 13 hectare lake with appropriate canal, channels, SBM and jetty facilities.

In addition to training and assessment courses, the ship's bridge simulators are also used for port design and accident investigation studies as well as government funded research projects, thereby making a significant contribution to the enhancement of safety of life at sea and effective ship operations.□

Chapter 1

TEAM MANAGEMENT

INTRODUCTION

The aim of the prudent mariner is to ensure that their ship reaches its destination safely and efficiently. To do this consistently demands a level of skill which is not easy to quantify but which needs to become part of the maritime culture, for there are about 80,000 ships trading internationally, each one sharing this common objective.

Like all knowledge-based skills, bridge watchkeeping and navigation require practice, support and reaffirmation. Left unattended they can become casual. The actions taken on the bridge may be uncritical and the interchange of information between the Master and the watchkeeping officers lapses into a working relationship where assumptions are made without being verified.

When bridge operations are loosely organised the impression can be given that things will be all right. However, when the unexpected occurs, confusion arises. It becomes more difficult to make decisions and the possibility exists for an error of judgement which might lead to an accident.

An accident by its nature is unexpected, but most accidents occur because there is no system in operation to detect and consequently prevent one person making a mistake—a mistake of the type all human beings are liable to make.

This book on bridge team management addresses this issue by explaining how to prepare for safe well-planned navigation, which is directed by the Master, officers and crew in such a way that the ship is always conducted under positive control, supported by the pilot when one is taken.

It may be argued that the methods being put forward in the book are too demanding upon manpower or that there is insufficient time to plan the next voyage properly. Alternatively, it may be stated that the tasks to be performed are essential, but the resources are not available. This discussion cannot be resolved through opinions. They differ widely. The issues can only be resolved by assessing the requirements to ensure navigational safety and putting in place a system to meet those requirements.

Bridge team management is thus more than a concept. It is the implementation of a way of working which recognises that reliable and consistent standards can only be maintained if navigation is based upon sound principles and reinforced by effective organisation. In this context it is up to all ships' officers to make the best possible use of available resources, both human and material, to achieve the successful completion of the voyage.

It is true that modern electronic systems can be used to automate bridge tasks and thereby alter the balance of duties performed on the bridge. However, this balance depends upon systems design, reliability and the knowledge of the officers to use it properly. Assumptions must not be taken for granted. The systems integrity must be assimilated into the bridge organisation so that there is no possibility of an undetected error occurring.

All members of the team have a part to play in this. The title 'Team Management' understates the interaction required within the team for such a system to work. It does not refer to an act of management by one person but a continuous adaptation of all the team members to fulfil the team roles that they have been assigned.

To achieve good results consistently, there are a number of factors which have to be addressed, notably those concerning technical knowledge and skills and also the requirements of the more traditional man-management or 'people' skills involved in the development of human resources.

In looking at the technical skills, consideration must be given to the techniques involved in preparing for and conducting the proposed voyage.

The skills concerning the development of human resources are covered in depth in other publications. The basic principles of good communication and man management are, however, important to the smooth and efficient running of any team, not just on the bridge of a ship. With current ship manning policies these skills must be developed to overcome cultural boundaries as well as those of a more traditional hierarchical rank structure.

Training and coaching

The ability to do a job well depends, to some extent, on the quality of the training a person has received. A poorly motivated trainer will often produce a poorly motivated trainee. We all spend a great part of our lives either imparting knowledge to others or being on the receiving end of such knowledge. This starts when we are very young and continues, no matter what our chosen vocation, throughout our lives. Proportionally, very little of this is conducted in the formal atmosphere of a learning establishment, most learning taking place at mother's knee or in the workplace. As such we are all teachers and we should not be shy of passing on knowledge when required.

The methods of passing on knowledge are many and various. They may be split into two main groups—training and coaching. These differ slightly in concept. Training a person involves instructing them in the execution of various tasks or procedures to a required standard. Coaching, however, involves the development of existing abilities through delegation and monitoring. It is a fine line between delegation for coaching purposes and abrogation of one's responsibilities!

Care should be taken to avoid delegating at too early a stage of development. If the 'trainee' is unprepared for the task, the effects can be devastating with a great deal of demoralisation and undermined confidence.

Training requirements for bridge tasks do not always lend themselves to direct training methods except perhaps in the case of very inexperienced personnel or for new concepts. The method of 'Sit next to Nelly and she will show you' is not always appropriate because it is a drain on already stretched human resources. This is where the concept of coaching is appropriate. With any coaching situation it is essential to maintain the supervision of the trainee and supply sufficient feedback on the progress being made. Lack of feedback reduces gains by the recipient.

The formation of a team from a selection of individuals may take a great deal of effort. Not all members will start with the same baseline of knowledge. Once the team is functioning, the flow of information will increase as a direct result of the newly found confidence of its members.

All team members should be kept fully aware of what is expected of them and their performance in their job frequently monitored and feedback given.

One of the primary functions of the team is the provision of a system of checking and cross-checking decisions which will directly or indirectly affect the conduct of the ship.

Wellbeing

The efficient team member will be both mentally and physically fit. Watchkeeping is often seen as being a passive role. Under certain low-key situations this may be the case. The watchkeeper can then be considered to be in a situation requiring only the maintenance of the present unstressed situation. This role changes dramatically in riskier situations, requiring more forceful action to prevent a situation arising, not merely responding to factors which may get out of control. This type of reaction requires both physical and mental wellbeing of a high standard.

Morale

A demoralised team, or even demoralised members of a team, are not going to produce the high standards required to ensure the continuing safety of the ship. Morale depends upon a large number of factors, but good teamwork and effective operation will be enhanced if the team members are clear as to their role in the team, can see the results of their own efforts, have their own deficiencies carefully corrected and are given credit when it is due.

ERROR CHAINS

Maritime incidents or disasters are very seldom the result of a single event, they are almost invariably the result of a series of non-serious incidents; the culmination of an error chain.

Situational awareness—i.e., knowing what is going on around the ship—helps the OOW recognise that an error chain is developing and taking such action, based upon this awareness, to break the error chain.

INDICATIONS OF ERROR CHAIN DEVELOPMENT

Certain signs in the function of a bridge team will indicate that an error chain is developing. This does not mean that an incident is about to happen; it does mean that the passage is not being carried out as planned and that certain elements of situational awareness may be lacking. The ship is being put at unnecessary risk and action must be taken to break the error chain.

AMBIGUITY

Ambiguity may be easily definable or there may be more subtle indications that things are not going as expected. In the event that two independent and separate position fixing systems—e.g., radar fix and GPS positions—do not agree, obviously something may be wrong with one of the fixes and immediate action is required to correct this ambiguity and determine which of the fixes is correct.

A more subtle variation of ambiguity may be that the echo-sounder reading does not agree with the charted depth. The less conscientious OOW may just accept this fact; another will not be satisfied and will try to determine why there is a difference between the expected and actual sounding.

Ambiguity may exist in that two team members do not agree upon a point of action. Ambiguity exists; of itself it may not be dangerous, but it means that there is a difference and the cause of this difference needs to be understood. One of the two team members is losing, or has lost, his situational awareness and an error chain may be developing.

The OOW may be aware that certain pre-agreed decisions—e.g., night orders, company procedures, etc.—are not being followed. Again, ambiguity exists. Why has there been deviation from the accepted procedures?

Ambiguity may be a result of inexperience or lack of training. The junior officer may feel that he is not in a position to voice his doubts. This should not be the case. Every member of a well-constructed, well-briefed team will feel confident that his doubts or fears can be expressed without his being reprimanded for what may turn out to be, in one instance an unwarranted worry, in another a very pertinent and situation saving remark.

DISTRACTION

Distraction, the full attention of a person upon one event to the exclusion of others or concentration upon what is often an irrelevancy can be an indication that situational awareness is beginning to break down, even if only for a restricted period. Distraction can be caused by an excessive workload, stress or fatigue, emergency conditions or, all too often, inattention to detail. It may also be caused by an unexpected, though not threatening event, such as a VHF call, which can occupy the full attention of a person to the exclusion of other more urgent needs.

INADEQUACY AND CONFUSION

A less definable indication of situational awareness is a feeling that the person concerned is losing control of the situation. A feeling that position fixing is not going as it should, that the person concerned does not know what is expected to happen next. This may be a result of lack of experience.

COMMUNICATION BREAKDOWN

Poor communications, both internal and external, are an indication that situational awareness may be at risk. Internal communications may be confused by physical causes such as noise, etc., or be caused by lack of common language or differing procedural methods. External communications breakdown may also be caused by non-common language or plain misunderstanding.

In any case, efforts must be made to overcome the cause of the communication breakdown, otherwise teamwork and mutual knowledge is at risk.

IMPROPER CONN OR LOOKOUT

Improper conning or poor lookout may be a result of lack of situational awareness as well as an indication of its breakdown. Within the bridge team organisation there can be no aspect more important than a safe conn and breakdown of this situation may lead to the ship being hazarded.

NON COMPLIANCE WITH PLAN

Non-compliance with the passage plan may result from the improper conn noted above, and is another indication that the situational awareness is breaking down.

PROCEDURAL VIOLATION

Unjustified departure from clearly defined and understood operating procedures must be recognised as a breakdown of situational awareness. As an example, the OOW of a ship which is proceeding in the wrong lane of a Traffic Separation Scheme must ask himsclf why hc is doing this. It will be off the planned track and is a direct violation of the International Regulations for Preventing Collisions at Sea; if he is both deviating from the track and ignoring the Rules then it is likely that he is not fully aware of the position of the ship.

CASUALTIES AND THEIR CAUSES

At the International Safety Conference (INTASAFCON III) held in Norway it was agreed that two principal factors seemed to be the main causes of collisions and groundings:—

WEAKNESSES IN BRIDGE ORGANISATION

and a result of such weakness

FAILURE TO KEEP A GOOD LOOKOUT

Weaknesses in bridge organisation have been a common failure in many casualties.

Such casualties may have been avoided by:

Setting double watches in appropriate circumstances;
Too often it is considered adequate to continue in a more complex situation with the same bridge manning levels as if the ship were deep sea with less immediate potential hazards.

Ensuring sufficient personnel are available in special circumstances
Additional personnel are often required to prepare equipment or to be available under certain circumstances. If calling them is left too late they may not become available until the ship is in the situation they could have helped prevent.

Precise instructions for calling the Master;
Too often the Master is called after a situation has irredeemably deteriorated. If the OOW is unclear as to when he should call the master then his indecision may lead to his not calling the Master.

Posting lookouts;
The OOW may consider that he alone can keep the lookout in addition to his own duties. Eventually, not posting a lookout may cause him to neglect other important duties.

Manning the wheel;
An unmanned wheel also requires the OOW to monitor and correct the steering. This, too, may cause him to overlook other duties.

An established drill for changing over from automatic to manual steering;
Despite the ease with which modern steering gear can be changed from one system to another, major incidents are on record where lack of awareness of the precise steering system in operation has led to disaster.

Precise instructions regarding reducing speed in the event of reduced visibility;
A busy OOW may not realise that the visibility has deteriorated, particularly at night. Even when he has realised that the situation has deteriorated he may not appreciate the increase in workload and consider that he can still cope.

The following features have been noticeable as causes of groundings:

Failure to pre-plan a track
Frequently it is not considered necessary to plan a track and show it on the chart. This may be because the mariners concerned feel that they know the area sufficiently well or because there is a pilot on the bridge.

Failure to monitor adequately the vessel's progress along the planned track
Although a planned track is shown on the chart OOWs do not always constantly and regularly fix the ship. This may lead to the OOW not being aware that the ship is deviating from track, perhaps towards danger.

Failure to take immediate action to regain track having deviated from it	Even when aware that deviation from the track is occurring, the attitude may be that it doesn't really matter, that there is enough safe water, when this is not actually the case.
Failure to cross-check fixes by comparing one means with another	If only one method of fixing is used when the ship is in constrained waters, mis-identification of a navigation mark or faulty electronic information, left unchecked and unobserved, may leave the OOW with a false sense of security.
Failure to use visual fixing when available	Electronic position fixing may sometimes be more accurate or convenient, but electronic fixes do not necessarily relate the ship's position to navigational hazards. Ignoring visual fixing can lead to the OOW becoming unaware of his changing environment.
Failure to use the echo-sounder when making a landfall or navigating in constrained waters	Except when alongside, the ship's nearest danger is almost invariably vertically below. Although it cannot be considered to be a position fix, observation and appreciation of the under-keel clearance can often warn the observer of approaching danger or that the ship is not in the position that it should be.
Failure to identify correctly navigational lights	An observer may convince himself that he sees the light he is looking for, not the light he is actually looking at. This mis-identification can lead to subsequent error or confusion.
Failure to ensure that important navigational decisions are independently checked by another officer	By their very nature all human beings are likely to make errors. It is essential that such human errors cannot occur without being noticed and corrected. An integral part of the navigational plan and bridge organisation must be to minimise the risk of such errors going unnoticed.

Most of the instances cited above are arrived at by the OOW not appreciating the complexity of his role in a deteriorating situation.

This may be because such responsibilities may never have been made clear to him or her.

BRIDGE ORGANISATION

An efficient bridge organisation will include procedures that:

1 Eliminate the risk that an error on the part of one person may result in a disastrous situation

2 Emphasise the necessity to maintain a good visual lookout and to carry out collision avoidance routines

3 Encourage the use of all means of establishing the ship's position so that in the case of one method becoming unreliable others are immediately available.

4 Make use of passage planning and navigational systems which allow continuous monitoring and detection of deviation from track when in coastal waters

5 Ensure that all instrument errors are known and correctly applied

6 Accept a pilot as a valuable addition to a bridge team

Individual Role

These procedures can only be achieved by each member of the bridge team realising that he has a vital part to play in the safe navigation of the ship and that safety depends upon all personnel playing their part to the utmost of their ability.

Each team member must appreciate that the safety of the ship should never depend upon the decision of one person only. All decisions and orders must be carefully checked and their execution monitored. Junior team members must never hesitate to question a decision if they consider that such a decision is not in the best interests of the ship.

THE PLAN

Voyages of whatever length, can be broken down into two major stages.

PREPARATION

EXECUTION

Included in **PREPARATION** is:

APPRAISAL

PLANNING

EXECUTION of the voyage includes

ORGANISATION

MONITORING

Chapter 2
PASSAGE APPRAISAL

Before any voyage can be embarked upon or, indeed, any project undertaken, those controlling the venture need to have a good idea of the risks involved. The appraisal stage of passage planning examines these risks. If alternatives are available, these risks are evaluated and a compromise solution is reached whereby the level of risk is balanced against commercial expediency. The appraisal could be considered to be the most important part of passage planning as it is at this stage that all pertinent information is gathered and the firm foundation for the plan is built. The urge to commence planning as soon as possible should be resisted. Time allocated to appraisal will pay dividends later.

INFORMATION SOURCES

The Master's decision on the overall conduct of the passage will be based upon an appraisal of the available information. Such appraisal will be made by considering the information from sources including:

1. *Chart Catalogue*
2. Navigational charts
3. *Ocean Passages for the World*
4. Routeing charts or pilot charts
5. *Sailing Directions and Pilot Books*
6. *Light Lists*
7. *Tide Tables*
8. Tidal stream atlases
9. Notices to Mariners (Navareas, Hydrolants, Hydropacs)
10. Routeing information
11. Radio signal information (including VTS and pilot service)
12. Climatic information
13. Load-line chart
14. Distance tables
15. Electronic navigational systems information
16. Radio and local warnings
17. Owner's and other unpublished sources
18. Draught of vessel
19. Personal experience
20. *Mariner's Handbook*

These items are discussed in some detail below. Only British and American catalogue numbers are quoted. Other, similar, publications may be available from other national sources.

1 CHART CATALOGUE   Published annually by the Hydrographer to the Navy (British) as NP 131 and by the Defence Mapping Agency (US) as CATP2V01U.

2 CHARTS   Many merchant ships carry British charts published by the Hydrographer of the Navy. However, there are areas of the world where the mariner may well be advised to consider using locally published charts as well. British Admiralty policy is to chart all British home and most Commonwealth and some Middle Eastern waters on a scale sufficient for safe navigation. Elsewhere the policy is to publish such charts as will enable the mariner to cross the oceans and proceed along the coasts to reach the approaches to ports. Along many coasts not covered in detail by British charts the mariner may find it better to use the charts of the hydrographic office of the relevant country.

Both US and Canadian regulations require that vessels in their waters must carry and use the appropriate charts. This means that the vessel's chart outfit may not meet the regulations. Navigators need to ensure that they have the correct charts.

Approximately 50 countries are listed as having established hydrographic offices publishing charts of their national waters. Addresses of the agents appointed by such offices may be obtained from *The Catalogue of Agents for the Sale of Charts*, published by the
> International Hydrographic Bureau,
> 7 Avenue President J. F. Kennedy,
> BP 445, MC98011
> Monaco Cedex,
> Principaute de Monaco.

International standard chart symbols and abbreviations allow foreign charts to be used with little difficulty but care must be taken to establish the chart datums used.

3 OCEAN PASSAGES FOR THE WORLD

Published by the Hydrographer of the Navy (British) as NP 136; contains information on planning ocean passages, oceanography and currents.

4 ROUTEING CHARTS & PILOT CHARTS

Routeing charts are published by the Hydrographer of the Navy (British) as Charts Nos. 5124-8. These are similar to the Pilot Charts published by the Defence Mapping Agency (USA). (see Atlases NVPUB105-9 & PILOT16 and PILOT55).

Both series give monthly information on ocean routeing, currents, winds and ice limits and various meteorological information.

5 SAILING DIRECTIONS AND PILOT BOOKS

British pilot books are published in 74 volumes by the Hydrographer of the Navy and give worldwide coverage.
Sailing directions are published by the Defence Mapping Agency (USA) in the series SDPUB 121-200. Some of these books are referred to as Planning Guides, giving information essentially the same as the British *Ocean Passages for the World*, others as Enroute, giving similar information to the British pilot books.

6 LISTS OF LIGHTS AND FOG SIGNALS

Published by the Hydrographer of the Navy (British) in 11 volumes (NP74-84) giving world wide coverage.

Seven volumes of *Light Lists* are published by the US Coast Guard, (COMDTM165021-7) giving details of all US coastal lights, including the Great Lakes. DMA publications LLPUB110-6 cover the rest of the world.

7 TIDE TABLES

Published by the Hydrographer of the Navy (British), annually, in three volumes, covering the world. Tidal times and heights may be readily obtained by using a computer program published by the British Admiralty (SHM-159A).

Worldwide tide tables are also published by the US National Ocean Service (NOSPBTT . . .)

8 TIDAL STREAM ATLASES

Published by the Hydrographer of the Navy (British), these atlases cover certain areas of North West Europe and Hong Kong.

Tidal current tables are published by the US National Ocean Service, covering the Atlantic coast of North America and the Pacific coast of North America and Asia. Tidal current charts are published by the US National Ocean Service for four major US ports.

9 NOTICES TO MARINERS

Notices to Mariners are published in weekly editions by both the British and US hydrographic authorities, enabling ships to keep their charts and other publications up to date.

10 SHIPS' ROUTEING

Published by IMO, this publication gives information on all routeing, traffic separation schemes, deep water routes and areas to be avoided which have been adopted by IMO. Routeing information is also shown on charts and is included in the sailing directions.

11 RADIO SIGNAL INFORMATION

The (British) *Admiralty List of Radio Signals* consists of seven volumes of text and four booklets of diagrams covering the following:

Vol 1 (1 & 2) coast radio stations, Inmarsat, GMDSS, SAR, Ship reporting systems.

Vol 2 radio navigational aids, RDF stations, radar beacons, time signals, electronic position-fixing systems.

Vol 3 radio weather services and navigation warnings.

Vol 4 meteorological observation stations.

Vol 6 (1 & 2) port operations, pilotage services and vessel traffic management and information services.

Similar information is available in US DMA publication RAPUB117.

12 CLIMATIC INFORMATION

Climatic information is available from a variety of sources including the pilot books, pilot charts and *Ocean Passages for the World* already mentioned. The British Admiralty book *Meteorology for Mariners* gives further general information.

13 LOAD LINE CHART

Load Line Rules are mandatory and the load line zones are shown in *Ocean Passages for the World* or BA Chart D6083.

14 DISTANCE TABLES

Both Ocean and Coastal Distance Tables are available from a variety of sources including British Admiralty (NP350) and US DMA publications NVPUB151 and NOSSPBPORTSDIST.

15 ELECTRONIC NAVIGATION SYSTEMS HANDBOOKS

Information required will depend upon the systems in use on the particular ship and should have been supplied with the equipment.

16 RADIO AND LOCAL WARNINGS

The latest information available on changes to navigation aids, etc., will be obtained from radio (including Navtext) and local warnings and must always be made available to those responsible for appraisal and planning. Local information is often available from the harbour authority.
For information on the worldwide navigational services and the transmitting stations see *Admiralty List of Radio Signals Vol 3*.

17 DRAUGHT OF SHIP The anticipated draught and trim of the ship at different stages of the passage will need to be known in order to calculate the under-keel clearance when in shallow water. The extreme height of the ship above the waterline, known as the air draught, may also be required.

18 OWNER'S AND OTHER SOURCES Supplementary information from the vessel's owners should be consulted, when available, as should reports from other vessels, information from agents and port authority handbooks, regulations and guides to port entry.

19 PERSONAL EXPERIENCE The personal experiences of crew members who have been to the anticipated ports and areas may prove of value.

20 THE MARINER'S HANDBOOK Published by the Hydrographer of the Navy (British), this book contains information of general interest to the mariner.

Having collected together all the relevant information the Master, in consultation with his officers, will be able to make an overall appraisal of the passage.

OCEAN The passage may be a transocean route in which case the first consideration will need to be the distance between ports, the availability of bunkers and stores, etc.

A great circle is the shortest distance but other considerations will need to be taken into account.

Meteorological conditions will need to be considered and it may well prove advantageous to use one of the weather routeing services. Although the recommended route may be longer in distance it may well prove shorter in time and the ship suffer less damage.

Ocean currents may be used to advantage, favourable ones giving the ship a better overall speed thus offsetting the disadvantage of taking a longer route.

Weather systems also need to be considered—e.g., a ship in the China Sea in summer needs plenty of sea room if it is liable to be involved in a tropical revolving storm and a passage in high latitudes may require ice conditions to be considered.

Irrespective of the advantages of using a preferred track, the Load Line Rules must always be obeyed. In certain circumstances, often political, a ship may need to keep clear of specified areas.

COASTAL The main consideration at the appraisal stage will be to determine the distance tracks should be laid off coastlines and dangers. When the ship is passing through areas where IMO-adopted traffic separation and routeing schemes are in operation, such routeing will have to be followed. In some coastal areas minimum distances off for specified vessels is determined by the relevant State.

Some shipping companies may also specify minimum distance off.

In archipelagos, it will be necessary to determine which straits and passages are to be used and whether or not pilotage is required. Under certain circumstances it may be preferable to divert around an archipelago.

Having made his appraisal of the intended voyage, whether it is a short coastal passage or a major transocean passage, the master will determine his strategy and then delegate one of his officers to plan the voyage. On most ships this will be the Second Mate, on some a designated navigating officer, on others the Master may have to do his own planning. Irrespective of who actually does the planning, it has to be to the requirements of the Master, who carries the final responsibility for the plan.

The plan needs to include all eventualities and contingencies.

Passage plans are often made from pilot station to pilot station but

IMO Resolution A.285(VIII), Annex A (v), subsequently incorporated in the STCW Convention 1978, Regulation II/1 states:

Despite the duties and obligations of a pilot, his presence on board does not relieve the officer in charge of the watch from his duties and obligations for the safety of the ship

This makes it quite clear that it is necessary to plan from berth to berth even though it is anticipated that there will be a pilot conducting the vessel at certain stages of the voyage.

Chapter 3

PASSAGE PLANNING

Planning may be considered in two stages:

        a)   ocean and open water;
        b)   coastal and estuarial;

though, at times, these two stages will merge and overlap.

CHARTS

Collect together all the charts for the intended voyage, putting them into the correct order. Charts not absolutely necessary for the voyage but which are adjacent to the area to be traversed should be included, as should very large scale charts—e.g., port plans on the coastal part of the voyage. Although it may not be necessary actually to use such charts, they may include information which could prove of use during the voyage. Ensure that all charts and publications have been corrected to the latest Notice to Mariners available and that any authentic Navwarnings, etc., received from any source are also included. (See Annex 2) Similar corrections may also have to be made during the voyage after the plan has been completed and the plan may have to be subsequently modified.

NO-GO AREAS

Coastal and estuarial charts should be examined and all areas where the ship **cannot** go carefully shown by highlighting or cross-hatching, taking care not to obliterate information—e.g., a navigation mark or a conspicuous object. Such areas are to be considered as no-go areas. In waters where the tidal range may not be very large, no-go areas will include all charted depths of less than the ship's draught.

In confined waters, where the tidal height may have a large influence, such no-go areas will vary according to the time of passage. Initially all areas and dangers showing charted depths of less than the draught plus a safety margin should be considered no-go, though such no-go areas may subsequently be amended when the actual time of passage is known.

Diag. 1 shows no-go areas for a ship on a draught of 9.1 metres, approximating to the 10 metre contour, no allowance being made for tidal height.

MARGINS OF SAFETY

Before tracks are marked on the chart the clearing distance from the no-go areas needs to be considered. When a fix is plotted on a chart it invariably represents the position of a certain part of the ship's bridge at the time of the fix. With large ships, although the plotted fix at a certain time may be outside a no-go area, it is possible that another part of the ship may already be in it—with disastrous results. A safety margin is required around the no-go areas at a distance that, in the worst probable circumstances, the part of the ship being navigated (the bridge) will not pass.

Among the factors which need to be taken into account when deciding on the size of this 'Margin of Safety' are:

1   The dimensions of the ship.
2   The accuracy of the navigational systems to be used.
3   Tidal streams.
4   The manoeuvring characteristics of the ship.

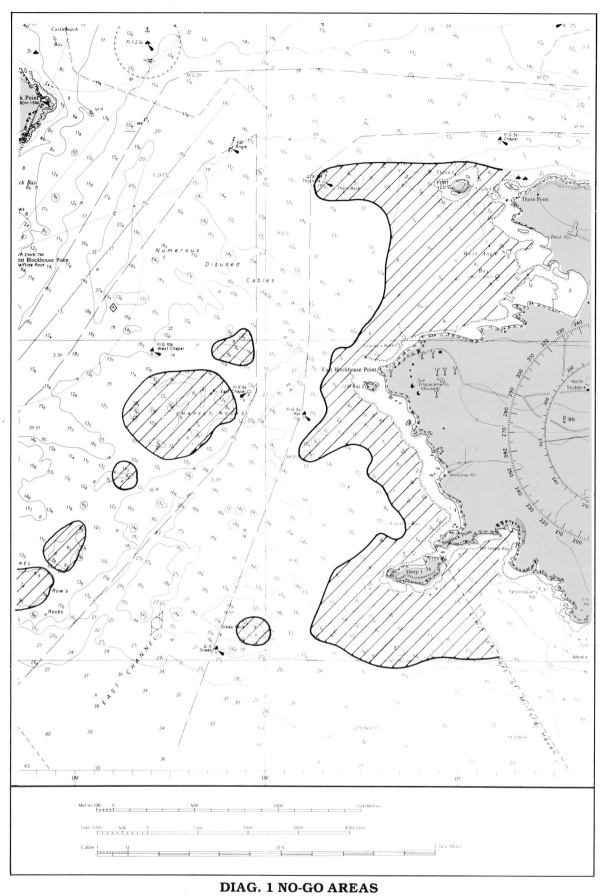

DIAG. 1 NO-GO AREAS
Assuming ship on maximum draught 9.1 metres
Crown copyright. Reproduced from Admiralty Chart 3274 with the permission of
the Hydrographer of the Navy

The margins of safety should be chosen so that they can be readily monitored. To achieve this they need to be related to one of the navigation systems in use (e.g., clearing bearings related to a headmark or parallel indexes).

Margins of safety will show how far the ship can deviate from track, yet still remain in safe water (see below). As a general rule the margin of safety will ensure that the ship remains in waters of a depth greater than draught + 20%. It is stressed that this is only a general rule, circumstances may dictate that the 20% clearance will need to be considerably increased —e.g.

1 Where the survey is old or unreliable.
2 In situations where the ship is pitching or rolling.
3 When there is a possibility that the ship may be experiencing squat.

SAFE WATER

Areas where the ship may safety deviate are considered to be safe water and the limits of this safe water are bounded by margins of safety.

OCEAN AND OPEN WATER TRACKS

Ocean and open-water tracks should first be drawn on the small-scale charts, according to the decisions made at the appraisal stage regarding the route to be taken. Great circle and composite great circle tracks will have to be calculated or obtained from the Satnav computer or from great circle charts; rhumb lines may be drawn straight on to the Mercator chart, but all tracks will have to conform to the limits determined at the appraisal.

COASTAL AND ESTUARIAL TRACKS

Coastal and estuarial tracks will also be constrained by the decisions made at the appraisal stage and should be first drawn on the small-scale charts covering large portions of the coastline, preferably from the departure port to the arrival port. This will depend upon the proximity of the ports and the charts of the area and, in most cases, more than one chart will have to be used. These first tracks will form the basis of the plan and from them may be obtained distances and steaming times. When the departure time is known, the ETA (Estimated Time of Arrival) at the various waypoints *en route* can be established.

The True direction of the track should be shown in close proximity to the track. This will not necessarily be the course steered to make this track; it only indicates the direction to make good. The course to steer will depend upon various factors at the time of making the passage.

When completed, these tracks should be transferred to and drawn on the large-scale charts of the area to be traversed. Transfer of a track from one chart to another must be done with great care.

To ensure that no mistakes are made, it is good practice doubly to check this operation by using a range and bearing of the transfer position from a readily identifiable object—e.g., a light common to both charts—and confirming this position on both charts by the latitude and longitude of the point.

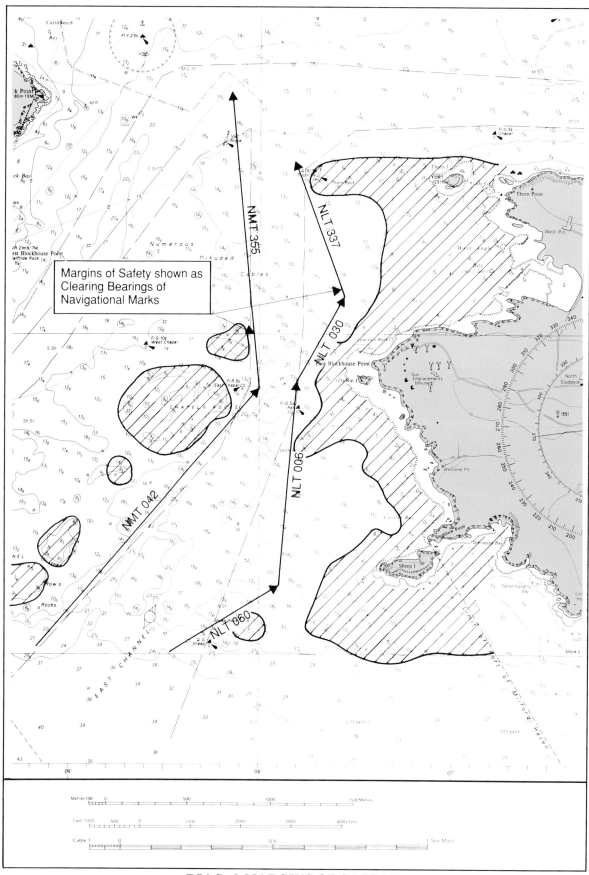

Margins of Safety shown as
Clearing Bearings of
Navigational Marks

DIAG. 2 MARGINS OF SAFETY
(for definition of Clearing Bearings see glosssary)
Crown copyright. Reproduced from Admiralty Chart 3274 with the permission of
the Hydrographer of the Navy

CHART CHANGE

It should be quite clearly shown on a chart the position where it is required to transfer to the next chart, giving the next chart's number.

TRACK CONSIDERATIONS

As a general rule there is nothing to be gained by closely approaching a danger other than to reduce passage distance and, consequently, steaming time. Even so, when it does become necessary to approach a danger there are general minimum rules that should be followed. The ship always has to remain in safe water (see below) and remain sufficiently far off a danger to minimise the possibility of grounding in the event of a machinery breakdown or navigational error.

DISTANCE OFF

It is not possible to lay down hard and fast rules regarding the distance off a danger that a ship should maintain; it will depend on:

1   The draught of the ship relative to the depth of water.

2   The weather conditions prevailing; a strong onshore wind or the likely onset of fog or rain will require an increase in distance off.

3   The direction and rate of the tidal stream or current.

4   The volume of traffic.

5   The age and reliability of the survey from which the information shown on the chart has been derived.

6   The availability of safe water.

The following guidelines will help in determining just how far to pass off dangers.

Where the coast is steep to and offshore soundings increase quickly, the minimum passing distance should be $1\frac{1}{2}$-2 miles.

Where the coast shelves and offshore soundings increase gradually, the track should ensure that adequate underkeel clearances (UKC) are maintained.

As a guideline:

Vessel's draught 3-6 metres, pass outside 10-metre contour;

Vessel's draught 6-10 metres, pass outside 20-metre contour;

Vessels with a draught of more than 10 metres must ensure that there is sufficient underkeel clearance, exercising due caution.

Irrespective of the safe UKC, a ship in a situation where the nearest navigational danger is to starboard must allow manoeuvring space to allow alteration of course to starboard for traffic avoidance.

REGULATIONS

Both company and national regulations regarding offshore distances must also be observed.

DEVIATION FROM TRACK

Ideally the ship will follow the planned track but under certain circumstances it may be necessary to deviate from such track—e.g., having to alter for another ship. Even so, such deviation from track should be limited so that the ship does not enter areas where it may be at risk or closely approaching the margins of safety.

UNDERKEEL CLEARANCE

In certain circumstances a ship may be required to navigate in areas with a reduced underkeel clearance. It is important that the reduced UKC has been planned for and clearly shown. In cases where the UKC is less than 10% of the deepest draught, or other such percentage as was agreed at the appraisal stage, then it is not only necessary that the OOW is aware of such UKC but also that he is aware that speed needs to be reduced in order to reduce squat with its consequent reduction in draught.

TIDAL WINDOW

In tidal areas, adequate UKC may only be attainable during the period that the tide has achieved a given height. Outside that period the area must be considered no-go. Such safe periods, called the tidal window, must be clearly shown so that the OOW is in no doubt as to whether or not it is safe for the ship to proceed.

STREAM/CURRENT ALLOWANCE

In open sea situations track correction is often made after the ship has been set off track by the tidal stream and/or current.

Such correction may be adequate in offshore situations, where the ship is not close to danger, but as the planned track approaches the coast it is better to make tidal and current correction prior to its taking effect.

Current information, set and rate is often available on the chart though more detailed information is given in *Ocean Passages for the World*, routeing charts and pilot books (see Appraisal sections 3, 4 & 5). Currents vary according to their location and the season and may be influenced by changes in meteorological conditions.

Tidal information is available from charts, tide tables and tidal atlases, further local information being available in pilot books (see Appraisal sections 5, 7 & 8.) Tidal streams vary according to the time of high water and the phase of the moon (neaps and springs) and can be influenced by local meteorological conditions.

When the actual time of transit of a given area is known, the tidal heights and streams can be calculated and due allowances made for these streams in order to find the course to steer to achieve a planned track. As well as adjusting these allowances as the tidal stream varies according to location and time, the OOW must still carefully monitor the ship's position and adjust the course steered to maintain the planned track.

COURSE ALTERATIONS & WHEEL-OVER

In the open sea and offshore coastal waters when navigating on small-scale large-area charts, course alterations will usually coincide with the planned track intersections. This will not be the case in confined waters when navigating on large-scale charts and where the margins of safety may require the ship to commence altering course at the wheel-over position some distance before the track intersection in order to achieve the new planned track.

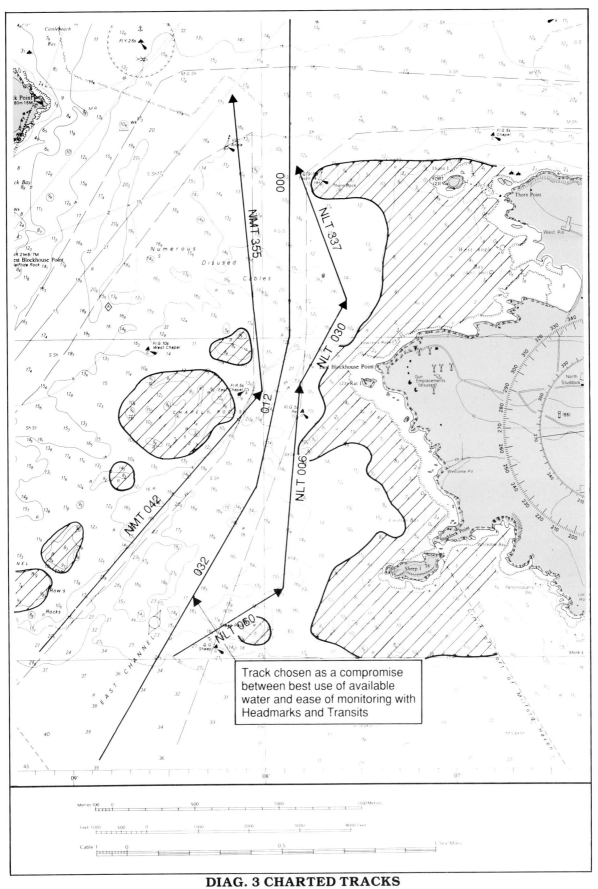

Track chosen as a compromise between best use of available water and ease of monitoring with Headmarks and Transits

DIAG. 3 CHARTED TRACKS
Crown copyright. Reproduced from Admiralty Chart 3274 with the permission of the Hydrographer of the Navy

Often such wheel-over positions will be determined by the pilot using his own judgement, based upon experience.

Planned wheel-over positions should be determined from the ship's manoeuvring data and marked on the chart. Suitable visual and radar cues should then be chosen to determine when the ship is at the wheelover position. The best cues for large alterations of course consist of parallel indexes or bearings parallel to the new track, whereas for small alterations a near beam bearing is often better.

Even when the pilot has the conn, the wheel-over position should be shown on the chart so that the OOW will be aware of its imminence and importance.

Diagram 4 shows the wheel over position using two separate methods of monitoring. At the course alteration from 032° to 012° the wheel-over position is achieved when Thorn Island is ahead at 1.31 miles (known as the dead range). At the course alteration from 012° to 000° the wheel-over position is achieved when the southern edge of Rat Island bears 096°.

PARALLEL INDEXING   The parallel index (PI) is a useful method of monitoring cross-track tendency in both poor and good visibility. It is a good practice to mark the planned PI on the chart inconspicuously at the planning stage. Like any radar technique, it is advisable to practise using PIs extensively in good visibility before placing total reliance on them when thick weather makes visual navigation methods impossible.

This simple and effective method of continuously monitoring a ship's progress is carried out by observing the movement of the echo of a radar-conspicuous navigation mark with respect to track lines previously prepared on the reflection plotter or by using ARPA index lines. It is most effective when the radar is in the north-up, relative motion mode.

A fixed radar target, such as a lighthouse or a headland, will apparently track past the own ship, depicted as being at the centre of the screen, as a line parallel and opposite to the ship's ground track. Any cross track tendency, such as may be caused by a tidal stream, will become apparent by the target moving off the parallel line.

The parallel index may also be used to monitor other events—e.g., wheel-over position. In this case the range and bearing of the target at the wheel-over point is marked on the PI. This also allows for a distance countdown to be made.

ARPA MAPPING   Many modern ARPAs have the facility to generate synthetic maps which can be stored in a retrieval system. In some instances, such maps may be stabilised through an electronic navigational system, but such facilities should be used in addition to and not to the exclusion of other systems.

WAYPOINTS   A waypoint is a position, shown on the chart, where a planned change of status will occur. It will often be a change of course but may also be an event such as:

1   End or beginning of sea passage.

2   Change of speed.

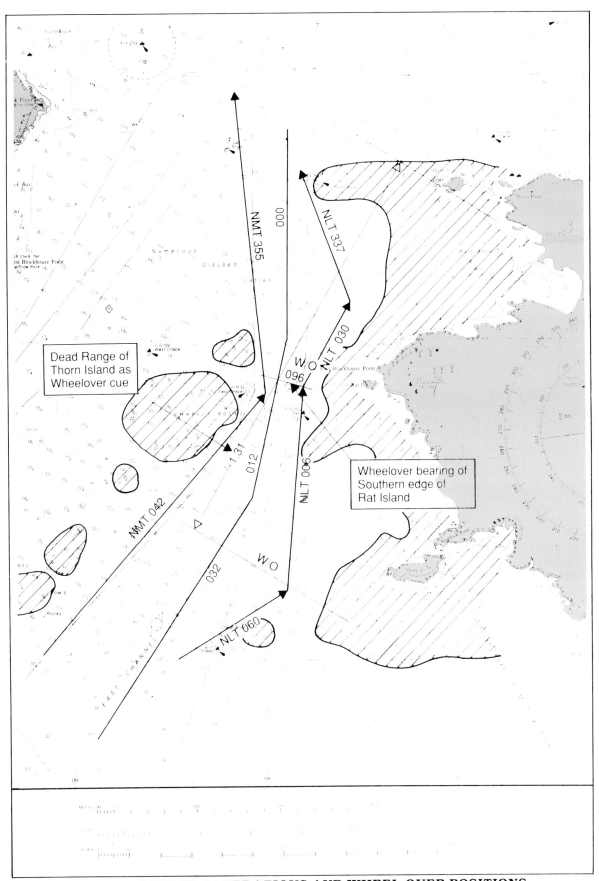

DIAG. 4 COURSE ALTERATIONS AND WHEEL-OVER POSITIONS
Crown copyright. Reproduced from Admiralty Chart 3274 with the permission of
the Hydrographer of the Navy

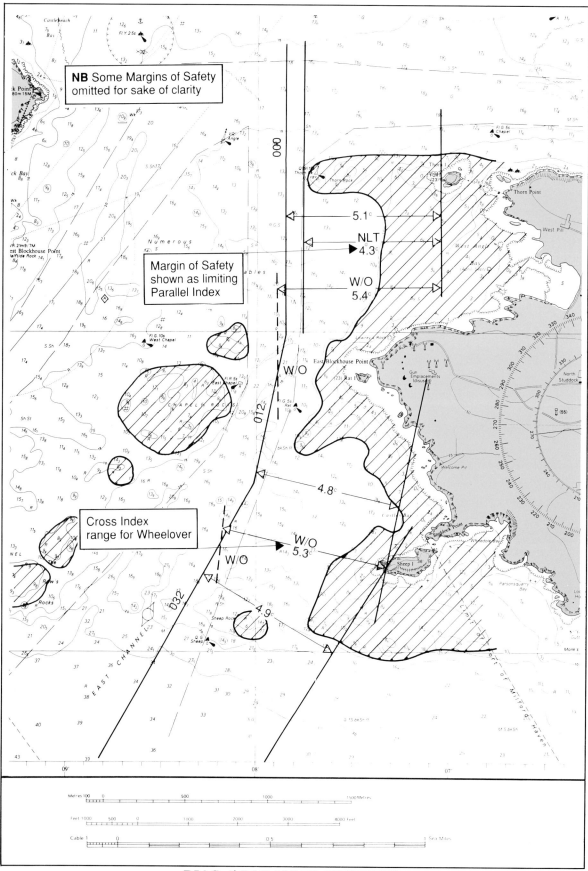

DIAG. 5 PARALLEL INDEXING
Crown copyright. Reproduced from Admiralty Chart 3274 with the permission of
the Hydrographer of the Navy

3   Pilot embarkation point.

4   Anchor stations etc.

Waypoints may also be used as useful reference points to determine the ship's passage time and whether or not a schedule is being maintained, particularly when they have been included in the appropriate electronic navigational system. Where an electronic navaid which stores waypoint information is in use, care should be taken to ensure that waypoint designators remain uniform throughout the plan.

**ABORTS &
CONTINGENCIES**

No matter how well planned and conducted a passage may be, there may come the time when, due to a change in circumstances, the planned passage will have to be abandoned.

ABORTS

When approaching constrained waters the ship may be in a position beyond which it will not be possible to do other than proceed. Termed the point of no return, it will be the position where the ship enters water so narrow that there is no room to return or where it is not possible to retrace the track due to a falling tide and insufficient UKC.

Whatever the reason, the plan must take into account the point of no return and the fact that thereafter the ship is committed. A position needs to be drawn on the chart showing the last point at which the passage can be aborted and the ship not commit herself. The position of the abort point will vary with the circumstances prevailing—e.g., water availability, speed, turning circle, etc.—but it must be clearly shown, as must a subsequent planned track to safe water.

The reasons for not proceeding and deciding to abort will vary according to the circumstances but may include:

1   Deviation from approach line.

2   Machinery failure or malfunction.

3   Instrument failure or malfunction.

4   Non availability of tugs or berth.

5   Dangerous situations ashore or in the harbour.

6   Any situation where it is deemed unsafe to proceed.

CONTINGENCIES

Having passed the abort position and point of no return, the bridge team still needs to be aware that events may not go as planned and that the ship may have to take emergency action. Contingency plans will have been made at the planning stage and clearly shown on the chart, so that the OOW does not have to spend time looking for and planning safe action when his duties require him to be elsewhere.

Contingency planning will include:

1   Alternative routes.

2   Safe anchorages.

3   Waiting areas.

4   Emergency berths.

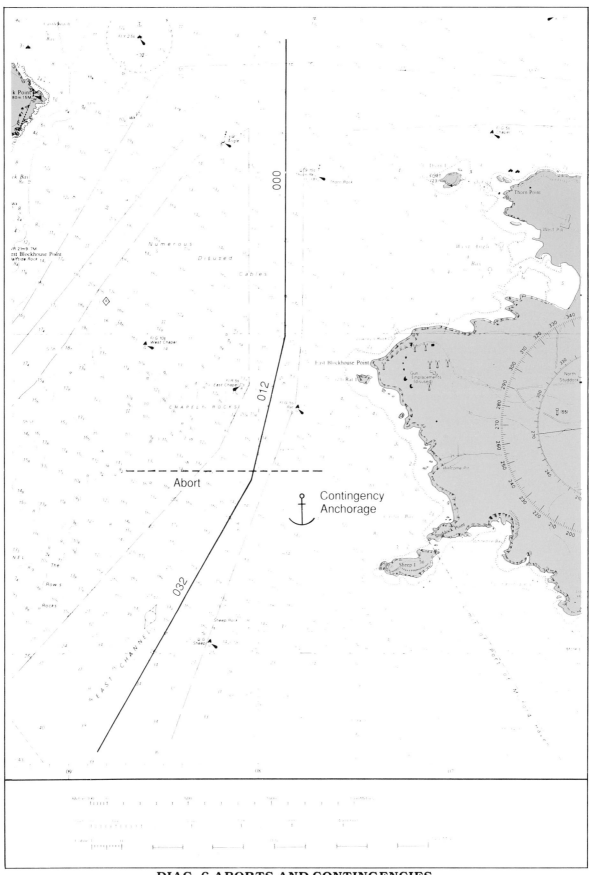

DIAG. 6 ABORTS AND CONTINGENCIES

Crown copyright. Reproduced from Admiralty Chart 3274 with the permission
of the Hydrographer of the Navy

It will be appreciated that emergency action may take the ship into areas where it is constrained by draught, in which case speed will have to be reduced; or tidally constrained, whereby it can only enter such areas within the tidal window. Such constraints must be clearly shown.

Having drawn no-go areas, the margins of safety and the track to be followed, the planning should now be concentrated on ensuring that the ship follows the planned track and that nothing will occur which is unexpected or cannot be corrected.

POSITION FIXING

A variety of position fixing methods is now available but it must not be assumed that any one of these methods will suit all circumstances.

PRIMARY AND SECONDARY POSITION FIXING

In order that the position fixing process is smooth, uneventful and clearly understood by all concerned, the passage plan will include information as to which fixing methods are to be used, which one is to be considered the primary method and which one(s) are to be used as backup or secondary. For example, whilst the ship is out of sight of land it may well be that the GPS is the primary system with Loran C as the secondary or back-up system. As the ship approaches the coast, the GPS will still be providing the primary fixing, the Loran C becoming less important and the radar fix confirming the GPS fix.

Eventually the Loran C, although running, will become redundant and more reliance placed on the radar fix with the GPS taking the secondary role. In enclosed waters the GPS position may become inappropriate and position fixing depend upon radar and visual methods. It is not possible to determine an invariable system; it depends upon the equipment available and the circumstances of the individual case. The important thing is that all concerned are aware that a system is in operation and that it should be followed as far as is practicable.

RADAR CONSPICUOUS OBJECTS & VISUAL NAVAIDS

In order to reduce the work load while navigating in coastal waters, the navigator will have determined and planned his primary and secondary methods of fixing. To reduce further the OOW's workload the navigator will have studied his chart at the planning stage and decided which radar conspicuous marks and visual aids are to be used at each stage of the passage.

LANDFALL LIGHTS

When making a landfall it should not be necessary for the OOW to have to examine the chart minutely to find which lights will be seen first. These should have been clearly shown on the chart so that the OOW can concentrate on actually looking for the light concerned, not looking on the chart trying to discover which lights should be visible.

The same applies when passing along a coastline or through constrained waters. All lights shown on a chart look similar and need to be studied to determine their individual significance. This needs to be done at the planning stage, not the operational stage when the OOW concerned may be too busy to spend time behind the chart table.

RADAR TARGETS	Similarly with radar targets—a little time spent at the planning stage will soon determine which are the targets to look for and use; a steep-to islet is going to be more reliable than a rock awash.
	Highlight on the chart Racons and other radar conspicuous object which will be used for position fixing. Highlight visual navaids as appropriate, differentiating between floating and fixed navaids and high-powered and low-powered lights.
BUOYAGE	Whenever buoys or other floating navmarks are being used as position fixing aids, their own position must be first checked and confirmed that they are as shown on the chart. In situations where buoy fixing is critical, such positions can be predetermined at the planning stage by noting their range and bearing from a known fixed object.
FIX FREQUENCY	Irrespective of the method of fixing to be used, it is necessary to establish the required frequency of the fixing. Quite obviously, this is going to depend on the circumstances prevailing; a ship close to danger will need to be fixed much more frequently than one in the open sea.
	As a guideline it is suggested that fixing should be at a time period such that it is not possible for a ship to be put into danger between fixes. If it is not possible to fix the position on the chart at such a frequency (fixes at intervals of less than three minutes can be very demanding) then alternative primary navigation methods—for example, parallel indexing —should be considered.
FIX REGULARITY	Having established the fix frequency, it is good practice to ensure that fixes are in fact made at that frequency, not as and when the OOW thinks fit. The only exception to this will be if the OOW has other priorities with which to contend— e.g., course alterations for traffic or approaching a critical wheel-over position. In this latter case, the ship's position should have been established immediately before the turn and again, as soon as possible, on completion.
ADDITIONAL INFORMATION	Although not essential to the safety of the ship, a lot of additional information can be shown on the plan which, by reminding the OOW of his obligations or reminding him to make certain preparations, will make the execution of the voyage simpler. Such information will include:
REPORTING POINTS	Reporting to the relevant authority as and where required can only make the vessel's routeing safer. Such reporting may also be compulsory.
ANCHOR CLEARANCE	Positions where anchor stations need to be called and the anchors cleared should be shown in order not to be overlooked.
PILOT BOARDING AREA	Timely preparation of the pilot ladder and warning to involved personnel to stand by as required.
TUG ENGAGEMENT	Reminder to OOW to call the crew necessary to secure tugs.
TRAFFIC AREAS	Areas where heavy traffic or where occasionally heavy traffic—e.g., ferries or fishing boats may be met.

Safe navigation of the ship does not only require fixing the position of the ship on the chart at regular intervals. The OOW needs to be constantly updating himself regarding the position of the ship relative to the required track and its tendency to increase or decrease its deviation from track. Although the regular fixing will give this information there are other, less obvious ways of obtaining such information, often requiring little input other than just observing natural features. Many of these can be planned in advance and marked on the chart:

TRANSITS (RANGES)

Transits (known as ranges in the USA)—i.e., the line on the chart upon which an observer would see two identifiable objects in line—can be used to give the OOW a quick indication of his position. Although it is only a single position line its advantage is that it requires no use of instruments but can be seen by eye. For extreme accuracy the distance between the observer and the nearer object should be no more than 3 times the distance between the objects observed, though transits of greater than this distance can be used to advantage.

Transits are sometimes printed on charts of inshore waters, but good use can be made of natural and clearly identifiable transits found at the planning stage and drawn on the chart.

Transits can also be used as a cue for a pre-arranged action to be taken—e.g., wheel-over,—or as a reminder than an event is about to occur.

COMPASS ERROR

Transits may be used to determine gyro and magnetic compass errors by comparing charted and observed bearings.

LEADING LINES

Leading lines are often shown on charts. In this case the transit printed on the chart is a track line to be followed to ensure that the ship passes clear of danger. By observing that the leads are in line the navigator is assured that his ship is on the planned track.

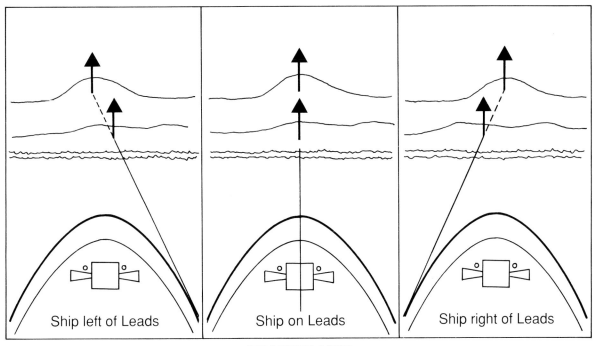

LEADING LINE

CLEARING MARKS	Clearing marks can be used to ensure that a ship is remaining within a safe area or is not approaching a danger. In diagram 7 the clearing mark is shown so that as long as the Western edge of Rat Island remains open of and to the left of Sheep Buoy then the ship is making a safe approach with reference to that side of the channel.
HEAD MARK	Often a ship is required to follow a track in narrow waters without the benefit of a leading line. In this case a suitable head marker should be selected. This should be a readily identifiable conspicuous object shown on the chart, which lies on the projection of the required track at that part of the passage. As long as the bearing of the head marker, corrected for errors and preferably taken with a centre line repeater, remains constant (i.e., the same as the required track), the ship is remaining on track. It should be noted that the ship need not necessarily be heading directly at the object, only that it is on the line of the required track. In most cases the ship's head will need to be offset to allow for tide or leeway.
CLEARING BEARINGS	In the event that no clearing marks are available a single identifiable charted object may be similarly used. In diagram 8, as the ship makes the approach track of 032°T it will remain safe as long as the fort on the Western end of Thorn Island remains within the range of bearings 028°T - 042°T. These clearing bearings should be shown on the chart as NLT 028°T and NMT 042°T (not less than / not more than).

Observing clearing bearings and clearing marks cannot be considered to be 'fixing' the ship but can assist the OOW in ensuring that his ship is not standing into danger. Similarly, using dipping distances, whilst not being considered to be an accurate fix, can make the OOW more aware that he is approaching danger. |
| **RANGE OF LIGHTS** | The maximum range at which a navigational light can be seen depends upon three separate factors:

1 The combined height of eye of the observer and the elevation of the light.

2 The intensity of the light.

3 The clarity of the atmosphere. |
| **GEOGRAPHICAL RANGE** | The greater the elevation of the light, the greater the distance at which it will be visible; equally, the greater the height of eye of the observer, the greater he will see the light. These two factors combined will give a maximum range of visibility called the geographical range and may be obtained from tables in the list of lights. In practice, this range will be severely reduced if the light observed is only low powered and therefore not capable of being seen at its geographical range. |

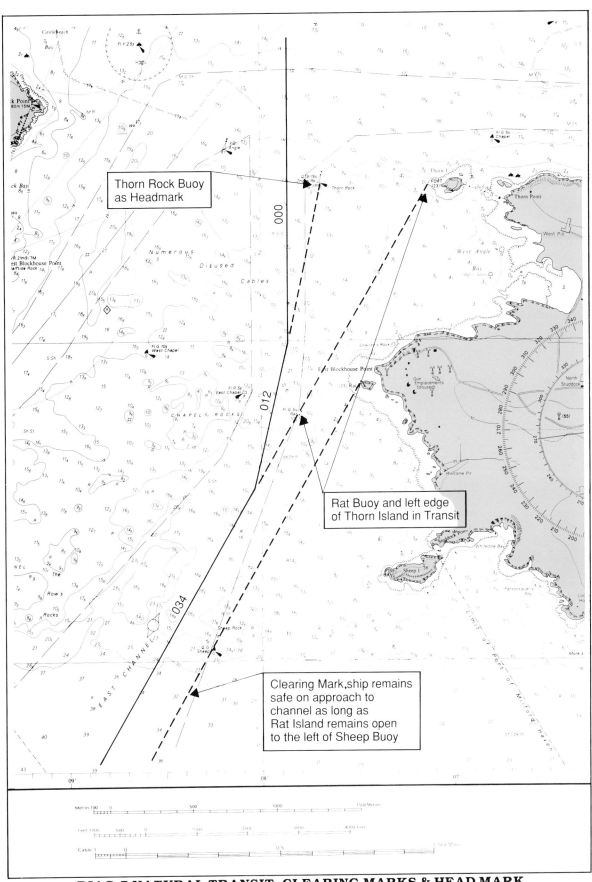

Thorn Rock Buoy
as Headmark

Rat Buoy and left edge
of Thorn Island in Transit

Clearing Mark, ship remains
safe on approach to
channel as long as
Rat Island remains open
to the left of Sheep Buoy

DIAG. 7 NATURAL TRANSIT, CLEARING MARKS & HEAD MARK
Crown copyright. Reproduced from Admiralty Chart 3274 with the permission of
the Hydrographer of the Navy

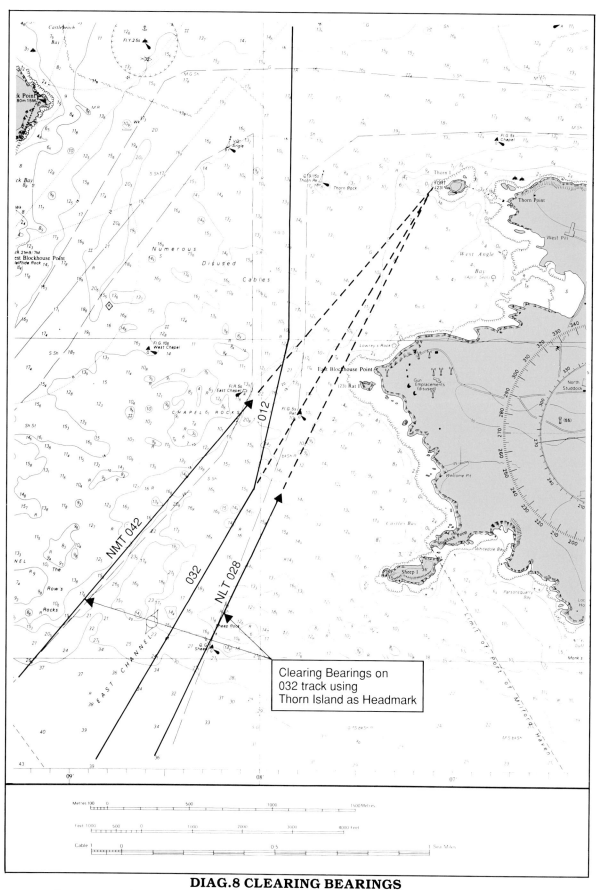

DIAG.8 CLEARING BEARINGS
Crown copyright. Reproduced from Admiralty Chart 3274 with the permission of
the Hydrographer of the Navy

LUMINOUS RANGE

This is the maximum distance at which the light can be seen and is dependent upon the intensity of the light and the atmospheric visibility prevailing. It takes no account of the height of the light nor that of the observer's eye. Obviously, the more intense the light, the further it will be seen, whatever the state of the atmosphere, and the appropriate table will give a good indication of how far the light can be expected to be seen.

NOMINAL RANGE

The range shown on the chart, beside the light star, is usually the nominal range—i.e., the luminous range when meteorological visibility is 10 miles. This is not invariable, though. Some countries, such as Japan, chart the geographical range: some, such as Brazil, the geographical or nominal according to whichever is the greater. It is the navigator's responsibility to make himself aware of which range is shown and to ensure that the OOWs are also aware of this fact.

LANDFALL LIGHTS

At the planning stage of the voyage, the navigator will have the opportunity to determine the maximum distance at which a landfall light should become visible. A comparison of the nominal and geographic ranges can be made and the lesser of the two selected as being the range at which the light should be seen, assuming meteorological visibility of at least 10 miles. It should be noted that only lights whose luminous range exceeds their geographical range can be considered as giving an approximate fix. In any case the arcs of maximum visibility should be drawn on the landfall chart so that the OOW is aware of the likelihood of seeing lights and which ones he should see first.

EXTREME RANGE

Approaching the coast, lights will come into view according to their height, their intensity and the ambient visibility.

Sometimes the first indications of the proximity of the coast will be powerful lights which may be seen before the radar can detect them as targets. Whilst not pretending that sighting the lights can be an accurate fix, an observation of the compass bearing at the time of sighting and plotting this with the extreme range of the light at this time will give the OOW an awareness of the proximity of danger.

In the event that a light is not sighted as expected, then the OOW will be aware that the ship is not where he anticipated it to be or that the light is unlit or obscured in cloud or that there is poor visibility between the ship and the light. The actual cause must be determined by his own judgement. The fact is that there is something not quite as it should be.

ECHO-SOUNDER

Some ships leave an echo-sounder running at all times. On ships where this is not the case, it is good practice to switch the echo-sounder on prior to a landfall being made. As in the case of a light at maximum range, whilst not providing a fix, the actual decrease in soundings will make the OOW more aware that he is approaching danger.

CHART OVERCROWDING

The information required to monitor the passage will, in many instances, be shown on the working charts. In some situations this may not be feasible, there may just be too much information needing to be shown, thus overcrowding the working area, or even blotting out certain chart details. In some cases this overcrowding can be reduced by writing the required information clear of the track—e.g., on the land—and drawing attention to it by either a connecting line or a reference letter.

PLANNING BOOK In any case, certain information may be better written in a planning book—e.g., times of high and low water, times of sunrise and sunset, VHF working frequencies. Where a ship uses a port regularly, the navigator may prefer to put the whole of his plan into a planning book in addition to the chart, so that it can be referred to at a later date.

CONNING NOTE BOOK Depending upon the length and complexity of the passage, or certain parts of it, it is good practice for an abbreviated edition of the plan to be made into a notebook so that the person having the conn, other than a pilot, can update himself as and when required without having to leave the conning position to look at the chart.

MASTER'S APPROVAL On completion the plan must be submitted to the Master for his approval.

PLAN CHANGES All members of the bridge team will be aware that even the most thorough plan may be subject to change during the passage. It is the responsibility of the person instigating such change to ensure that changes are made with the agreement of the Master and that all other members of the team are advised of such changes.

Chapter 4

EXECUTING THE PLAN

TACTICS

The plan having been made, discussed and approved, execution of the plan now has to be determined. By this is meant the methods used to carry out the plan, including the best use of available resources. Final details will have to be confirmed when the actual timing of the passage can be ascertained. The tactics to be used to accomplish the plan can then be agreed and should include:

ETAs for TIDE

Expected times of arrival at critical points to take advantage of favourable tidal streams.

ETA for DAYLIGHT

ETAs at critical points where it is preferable to make a daylight passage or with the sun behind the ship.

TRAFFIC CONDITIONS

Traffic conditions at focal points.

DESTINATION ETA

ETA at destination, particularly where there may be no advantage gained by early arrival.

TIDAL STREAMS

Tidal stream information, obtained from the chart or tidal stream atlases, can be included in the planned passage when the time of transit of the relevant area is known. Ideally, courses to steer should be calculated prior to making the transit, though in fact, strict adherence to the planned track will actually compensate for tidal streams.

Current information can also be obtained and shown on the chart.

PLAN MODIFICATION

It must always be borne in mind that safe execution of the passage may only be achieved by modification of the plan in the case of navigational equipment becoming unreliable or inaccurate or time changes having to be made—e.g., delayed departure.

ADDITIONAL PERSONNEL

In order to achieve safe execution of the plan it may be necessary to manage the risks by utilising additional deck or engine personnel. This will include an awareness of positions at which it will be necessary:

1 To call the Master to the bridge for routine situations such as approaching the coast, passing through constrained waters, approaching the pilot station, etc.

2 To change from unattended to manned machinery space.

3 To call an extra certificated officer to the bridge.

4 To make personnel, in addition to the watchkeepers, available for bridge duties such as manning the wheel, keeping lookout, etc.

5 To make personnel, in addition to the watchkeepers, available for deck duties such as preparing pilot ladders, clearing and standing by anchors, preparing berthing equipment, engaging tugs, etc.

BRIEFING

Before commencing the voyage there is considerable advantage to be gained by briefing all concerned. This may take place over a considerable period of time. As the actual commencement of the voyage approaches, certain specific personnel will have to be briefed so that work schedules and requirements can be planned.

In particular, any variation from the routine running of the ship—e.g., doubling of watches, anchor party requirements, etc., must be specifically advised to involved personnel, either by the Master or the navigator.

Such briefing will require frequent updating and at different stages there will have to be rebriefing as the voyage progresses. Briefing will make individuals aware of their own part in the overall plan and contributes to their work satisfaction.

FATIGUE

Prior to the commencement of the passage and, in certain cases, during the passage, it may be necessary for the Master to ensure that rested and unfatigued personnel are available. This could include such times as leaving port and entering very heavy traffic areas or bad weather conditions or high risk situations such as transiting a narrow strait, etc. This availability can be achieved, within the limits of the total number of persons available, by ensuring that watchkeepers of all descriptions are relieved of their duties well in advance of being required on watch in order that they may rest.

This may require changes to routine watchkeeping periods, extending certain watches or even curtailing watches, but it is at the Master's discretion and he should not hesitate to make such changes.

VOYAGE PREPARATION

One of the basic principles of management is ensuring that the workplace is prepared and readied for the ensuing task. This will normally be the task of a junior officer who will prepare the bridge for sea. Such routine tasks are best achieved by the use of a checklist, but care has to be taken to ensure that this does not just mean that the checklist is ticked without the actual task being done.

BRIDGE PREPARATION

At the time designated by the Master the officer responsible should prepare the bridge by:

1 Ensuring that the passage plan and supporting information is available and to hand. (It is likely that the navigating officer responsible for the construction of the passage plan will have made these items ready; nevertheless, they should still be confirmed.)

Charts should be in order, in the chart drawer and the current chart available on the chart table. It is bad practice to have more than one chart on the table at a time as information read from one and transferred to the other may not be correct.

2 Checking that chart table equipment is in order and to hand—e.g., pens, pencils, parallel rules, compasses, dividers, note pads, scrap pads, etc.

3 Checking that ancillary watchkeeping equipment is in

order and to hand—e.g., binoculars, azimuth rings, Aldis lamp, etc.

4   Confirming that monitoring and recording equipment—e.g., course recorder, engine movement recorder—is operational and recording paper replaced if necessary.

5   Confirming that the master gyro is fully operational and follow-ups aligned. The magnetic compass should be checked.

6   Checking that all instrument illumination lamps are operational and their light levels adjusted as required. The availability and whereabouts of spares should be checked.

7   Checking navigation and signal lights.

8   Switching on any electronic navigational equipment that has been shut down and operating mode and position confirmed.

9   Switching on and confirming the readouts of echo-sounders and logs and confirming associated recording equipment.

10 After ensuring that the scanners are clear, switching on and tuning radars and setting appropriate ranges and modes.

11 Switching on and testing control equipment—i.e., telegraphs, combinators thrusters and steering gear as appropriate.

12 Switching on and testing communications equipment both internal (telephones and portable radios) and external (VHF and MF radios, Navtex, Inmarsat and GMDSS systems as appropriate.)

13 Testing the whistle.

14 Ensuring that clearview screens and wipers are operational and that windows are clean.

15 Confirming that all clocks and recording equipment are synchronised.

16 Ensuring that the workplace is in correct order, lighting is as it should be, doors and windows open and close easily, temperature controls are set as appropriate and movable objects are in their correct place.

17 After ensuring that there is no relevant new information on the telex, fax or Navtex, advising the Master that the bridge is ready for sea.

The above list is only a general guide; each ship will have its own specific checks which have to be included. A modified version of the above should also be carried out when approaching port or any area where other than routine watchkeeping may occur.

Chapter 5

MONITORING THE SHIP'S PROGRESS

Monitoring is ensuring that the ship is following the pre-determined passage plan and is a primary function of the officer of the watch. For this, he may be alone; assisted by other ship's personnel; or acting as back up and information source to another officer having the conn.

Monitoring consists of following a series of functions, analysing the results and taking action based upon such analysis.

FIXING METHOD   The first requirement of monitoring is to establish the position of the ship. This may be done by a variety of methods, ranging from the very basic three bearing lines, through a more technically sophisticated use of radar ranges/bearings, to instant readout of one of the electronic position fixing systems—e.g., Decca, Loran or GPS. The result, though, is always the same. However the fix has been derived, you finish up with no more than a position. It is how this information is used that is important.

VISUAL BEARINGS   As stated above, fixing methods vary. Basic fixing consists of more than one position line obtained from taking bearings using an azimuth ring on a compass. Gyro or magnetic, the bearings are corrected to true, drawn on the chart and the position shown. Three position lines are the minimum required to ensure accuracy.

Poor visibility or lack of definable visual objects may prevent a three-bearing fix being made. In this case radar-derived ranges (distances) may be included in the fix and under some circumstances make up the whole of the fix. In any case a mixture of visual or radar bearings and radar ranges is acceptable. Other methods may be used—e.g., running fixes (which may be inaccurate as they depend on an element of DR) sextant angles, etc.—but these are seldom used on modern ships. Any good chartwork text book will give a wide range of less-used fixing methods.

Electronic position fixing may also be used, particularly where there are no shore-based objects to be observed and the radar coastline is indistinct. Whilst these systems appear to be infallible the operator needs to have a good understanding of the principles and failings of the electronic system being used, in order to avoid a false sense of security.

FREQUENCY   Fix frequency will have been determined at the planning stage. Even so, this may have to be revised, always bearing in mind the minimum frequency is such that the ship cannot be allowed to get into danger between fixes.

REGULARITY   Fixing needs not only to be accurate and sufficiently frequent, it also needs to be regular.

ESTIMATED POSITION   Regular fixing also allows a fix to be additionally checked. Each time a position has been fixed, it is good practice to estimate the position that the ship should have reached at the next fix. Providing fixing is being carried out at regular intervals this can easily be picked off as the distance between the present and the previous fix and checked against the anticipated speed. If the next fix coincides with the estimated position (EP), then this acts as an additional check that the ship is maintaining its track and speed.

Should the fix not coincide with the EP, then the OOW is aware that something is either wrong with the obtained position or some external influence has affected the ship. The first action is to check the EP, then check the fix. If they are both correct then something is influencing the ship; either the course being steered is not the one required or the engine revolutions have changed. If both these features are in order then some external influence is affecting the ship, either the wind has changed direction or strength or the tidal stream has changed. The OOW is immediately aware that something is influencing the ship and can take immediate action to correct it.

SOUNDINGS

It is also good practice to observe the echo-sounder at the same time as fixing and writing this reading on the chart beside the fix. If the observed reading is not the same as that expected from the chart then the OOW is immediately aware that something is not well. It may be that the chart is wrong; it may be that the ship is standing into danger.

CROSS TRACK ERROR

Having fixed the position the OOW will be aware of whether or not the ship is following the planned track and whether or not the ship will be at the next waypoint at the expected time. If the ship is deviating from the planned track he must determine whether or not such deviation will cause the ship to stand into danger and what action he should take to remedy the situation. Apart from deviating from track to avoid an unplanned hazard such as an approaching ship, there is seldom justification not to correct the deviation and get the ship back onto the planned track. The OOW must use his judgement as to how much he needs to alter course to return to track, bearing in mind that even when he has returned to the planned track he will need to leave some of the course correction on in order to compensate the cause of the earlier deviation.

INTERNATIONAL REGULATIONS FOR PREVENTING COLLISIONS AT SEA

Irrespective of the planned passage, no ship can avoid conforming with requirements of the 'Rule of the Road'. These rules are quite clear, are internationally accepted and understood by most OOWs.

Rule 16 states: 'Every vessel which is directed to keep out of the way of another vessel shall, so far as possible, take early and substantial action to keep well clear.'

Despite the requirement to maintain track, Rule 8 makes it quite clear that the give-way ship must keep clear, either by altering course or if this is impossible then by reducing speed, or a combination of both these factors. Proper planning will have ensured that the ship will never be in a situation where such action cannot be taken.

In areas of heavy traffic and proximity of dangers, the person having the conn will have to hold a delicate balance of other-ship avoidance and planned track maintenance. The priority will be to avoid collision, but not at the expense of a grounding.

NON-NAVIGATIONAL EMERGENCIES

Similarly, the bridge team must never allow the reaction to an emergency situation to so dominate their reaction that the ship is potentially hazarded by diverting into an area of high danger. Again, the planning should have allowed for such contingencies but even the best plan cannot allow for every conceivable situation. Situational awareness and careful assessment of the situation, coupled with principles of bridge team management will help prevent a bad situation compounding and becoming worse.

TIME MANAGEMENT

In the event that the ship is ahead of or behind the planned ETA at the next waypoint, the OOW must use his judgement as to whether he adjusts the speed or not. In some instances, as for example when it is imperative that the ship's ETA is critical to make a tide, then ETAs have to be adhered to.

In either of the instances cited above, it will be the practice of the ship or at the OOWs discretion as to whether he advises the Master.

LOOKOUT

The OOWs situational awareness will be improved by both the structured management of the team and his own self-discipline ensuring that he keeps a good professional watch. This will include his confirming that a good lookout is kept. A good lookout does not just mean that he personally keeps a good visual lookout of the ship's surroundings.

Rule 5 of the International Regulations for Preventing Collisions at Sea (1972, ratified 1977) states:

Every vessel shall at all times maintain a proper lookout by sight and hearing as well as by all available means appropriate in the prevailing circumstances and conditions so as to make a full appraisal of the situation and of the risk of collision.

Though specifically addressing collision the above-quoted rule also applies if the OOW is to maintain his situational awareness. The keeping of an efficient lookout needs to be interpreted in its fullest sense and the OOW needs to be aware that lookout includes the following items:

1   A constant and continuous all-round visual lookout enabling a full understanding of the current situation and the proximity of dangers, other ships and navigation marks to be maintained.

In some instances, particularly poor visibility, radar will give a better picture of the ship's environment than actual visual observation. However, unless the OOW has considerable experience of comparing the radar picture with the visual scene he cannot automatically interpret his radar picture. In any case, the visual scene is the real scene not an electronic version of reality and the OOW who frequently observes the scene outside the windows will have a better understanding of and feel for the world around him.

2   Visual observation will also give an instant update of environmental changes, particularly visibility and wind.

3   Visual observation of the compass bearing of an encroaching other-ship will quickly show whether or not its bearing is changing and whether or not it needs to be considered a danger.

4   Visual observation of characteristics of lights is the only way of positively identifying them and thus increases the OOWs situational awareness.

5   The lookout will also include the routine monitoring of ship control and alarm systems—e.g., regularly comparing standard and gyro compasses and that the correct course is being steered.

6   Electronic aids should not be overlooked or ignored, under any circumstances, but it should be borne in mind that echo-sounders, radars, etc., are aids to navigation, not merely single means of navigation.

7   Also included in the concept of lookout should be the advantageous use of VHF. Judicious monitoring of the appropriate channels may allow the ship to be aware of situations arising long before it is actually in the affected area.

8   A routine should be established for major course alterations including:

'a   Checking astern prior to altering.

b   Checking, both visually and by radar, along the bearing of the new track.

The OOW's situational awareness will also be enhanced by his observation of his environment using all available means, not just limiting himself to the routine of fixing and correcting as described above.

UNDER KEEL CLEARANCE   Routine observation of the echo-sounder should become one of the procedures of the watch.

WAYPOINTS   Besides being points noted on the chart where a change of status or an event will occur, waypoints are also good indicators of whether the ship is on time or not. If not, then something has occurred or is occurring which has affected the passage and the OOW will take steps to correct this occurrence.

TRANSITS (RANGES)   Transits are often important navigational features, they can, for example, be used to cue decisions such as a wheel-over, but can also be used in a more passive role. The OOW can use a transit to confirm that the ship is on schedule or that it is remaining on track, particularly when this occurs after an alteration. Of itself, the confirming transit may be no more than a minor occurrence but it will help the observant OOW confirm in his own mind that all is well and as it should be.

LEADING LINES   Leading lines—i.e., the transit of two readily identifiable land-based marks on the extension of the required ground track and usually shown on the chart—are used to ensure that the ship is safely on the required track.

NATURAL LEADING LINES

In some instances the OOW may be able to pick up informal leading lines—e.g., a navmark in line with an end of land which will confirm that the vessel is on track.

Observation of a head mark and a quick mental calculation will give an indication of the distance that the ship has deviated from her track.

$$\frac{\text{Required brg} \sim \text{observed brg x dist from object (Miles)}}{6} = \text{dist off track in cables}$$

Alternatively, the off-track distance can be readily evaluated by looking down the required bearing and estimating the distance between the headmark and where the observed bearing meets the land. Man-made features such as cars, buses and lamp posts can aid this estimate.

CLEARING MARKS & BEARINGS

As described in planning, clearing marks and clearing bearings, whilst not being considered to be a definitive fix, will indicate to the OOW that his ship is remaining in safe water.

RISING/DIPPING DISTANCES

Making a landfall or running along a coastline, observing rising and dipping distances of powerful lights and marking this on the chart with the observed bearing can also help assure the OOW that the ship is in the anticipated position.

LIGHT SECTORS

The changing colours of sectored lights can also be used to advantage by the OOW and in certain instances, which the OOW should be very aware of, will indicate that the ship is standing into danger. On occasion the flickering sector change can virtually be used as a bearing. Care needs to be taken in icy weather as sectors can become indistinct.

Chapter 6
TEAMWORK

IMO Resolution 285 requires that the OOW 'ensures that an efficient lookout is maintained' but concedes that 'there may be circumstances in which the officer of the watch can safely be the sole lookout in daylight.'

However: 'When the officer of the watch is acting as the sole lookout he must not hesitate to summon assistance to the bridge, and when for any reason he is unable to give his undivided attention to the lookout such assistance must be immediately available.' (Annex B 2.) It is normal practice to have the uncertificated watchkeeper working in the vicinity of the bridge where he can be called should he be required. At night the lookout is normally on the bridge carrying out his exclusive lookout duties.

Under certain conditions the OOW may be the only person actively engaged in the navigation of the ship. The steering may be in automatic and the lookout engaged in duties around the bridge area. There is no apparent call for teamwork; the OOW will be personally responsible for all aspects of safe navigation. Nevertheless, he will be required to work within a framework of standing and specific orders so that the Master will be confident that the watch is being kept to his, and the company's, standards.

The single watchkeeper status may change at short notice. If the OOW becomes engaged in duties which require him to forgo his obligations as lookout then he will have to call his unlicensed watchstander to take that role. Here we have the first basics of teamwork.

It is the responsibility of the OOW to ensure that the seaman assigned watchkeeping duties:

1 Has been properly instructed in lookout duties as to what is expected of him.

2 Knows how to report observations.

3 Is adequately clothed and protected from the weather.

4 Is relieved as frequently as necessary.

The watchkeeping officer may require a man on the wheel in addition to the lookout. It is the responsibility of the OOW to see that the vessel is safely and efficiently steered.

We are now in a situation requiring a fair amount of organisation and cooperation. The watch officer still has the responsibility for the watch but has to use and rely upon the assistance of two other people. It is his responsibility to ensure that they are aware of their duties and carry them out in a manner which will enhance the standard of the watch. Although neither person, in this case, should find the duties particularly onerous or difficult, the watch officer still needs to ensure that orders are correctly followed—e.g., helm orders are complied with as required, not as the helmsman thinks fit.

Under certain circumstances the OOW may find it is necessary to call the Master to the bridge. This may be because the preplanning requires the presence of the Master on the bridge or the Master's standing or night orders have required him to be called under the developing circumstances or because the OOW has realised that the situation needs the experience and expertise of the Master.

Calling the Master to the bridge will not transfer the conn from the watch officer to the master. Until such time as the Master actually declares that he has the conn the OOW must still carry out his duties as he was prior to the Master's arrival. Once the Master has taken the conn, and the event logged, then the watch officer moves into a supportive role, but is still responsible for the actions of his watch members.

It is now necessary to define the role of the individual team members. Quite obviously this will to a large extent depend upon the individuals involved and the practice of the ship, but unless each individual's role is understood by all involved there will be overlapping or a possible ignoring of certain functions. Teamwork will depend upon the following role suggestions being carried out.

The **Master** controls movement of the vessel in accordance with the Rule of the Road and recommended traffic schemes, regulates the course and speed and supervises the safe navigation of the vessel and co-ordinates and supervises the overall watch organisation.

The **Watch officer** continues to navigate the ship reporting relevant information to the Master, ensuring that such information is acknowledged. He will fix the vessel and advise the conn of the position and other information. He will monitor the execution of helm and engine orders, co-ordinate all internal and external communications, record all required entries in logbooks and perform other duties as required by the Master.

The lookout and helmsman will still be carrying out their duties, as above.

Under certain circumstances, the Master may consider it necessary to have the support of two navigating officers—one as OOW, the other as backup. The Master's responsibilities will be as above, but the responsibilities of the two officers will require careful definition.

It is obvious that a scenario requiring two watch officers supporting the Master will indicate that the ship is in a very high risk situation.

Probable factors will be:

1 Narrow margins of safety requiring very careful track maintenance.

2 Reduced underkeel clearance.

3 Heavy traffic.

4 Poor visibility; or any combination of similar factors.

The OOW will still carry out his duties as defined above and be generally responsible for the normal running of the watch.

The additional officer's role will be to provide the Master with radar-based traffic information and to giving general backup to the OOW on the chart. This will include providing the chart with navigational information as required, confirming important navigational decisions and coping with both internal and external communications.

It is difficult to establish hard and fast rules about how the tasks of the bridge team should be distributed. It will depend upon the abilities and characters of the personnel involved, the circumstances requiring the additional personnel involvement and the layout of the bridge. The important thing to bear in mind is that each member of the team knows the role that he is required to carry out and the roles of other members of the team. As stated above this will preclude unnecessary duplication of tasks and, more importantly, ensure that other tasks are not ignored or overlooked.

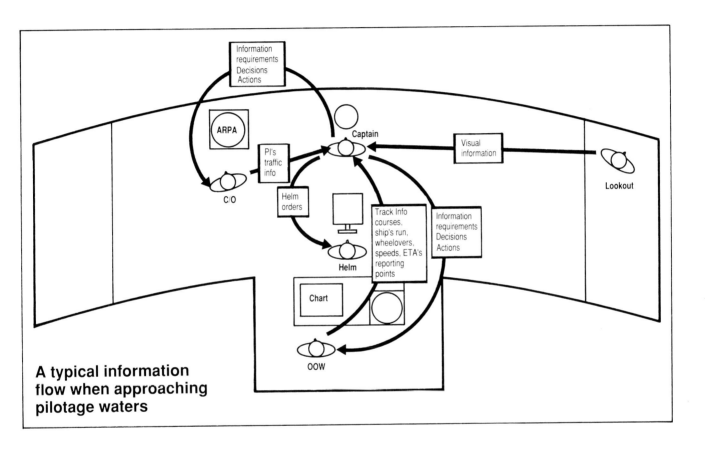

A typical information flow when approaching pilotage waters

INFORMATION FLOW BETWEEN CONNING OFFICER, OOW, ADDITIONAL OFFICER, LOOKOUT AND HELMSMAN
This information flow may be modified by bridge design, automation or regrouping of personnel—The information demands, however, remain the same.

ILLUSTRATIVE CASE STUDY

The time is 0100. The ship has made a safe landfall and is approaching the destination port. The ETA at the pilot station was confirmed at 1800 the previous evening and it was agreed that the pilot would board at 0300. The pilotage to the berth is expected to take about one hour. The weather is fine and clear and high water at the berth is at 0330, thus allowing the ship to berth on the first of the ebb.

The Second Mate is on watch with his standby rating and end of sea passage is scheduled for 0200. The Master has left night orders to be called at 0130. The anchors were cleared the prevous afternoon and the pilot ladder has been put on deck, ready for using on either side. The engine control room has been manned since 2200 and the engineers have been advised that EOP is at 0200.

The Second Mate is fixing the ship's position at 20-minute intervals using Loran C with visual bearing confirmation and is running a straight line parallel index on the radar for continuous off-track detection.

0130   The OOW calls the Master as per night orders, advising him that the voyage is going as scheduled and that there is light traffic in the vicinity.

       The OOW confirms with the engineroom that the ship is on schedule and that reduction from sea speed will still be at 0200.

       The OOW informs his standby man, at present acting as lookout, that they are approaching the port and to keep a careful lookout for small inshore craft such as fishing boats and that an additional crewmember will be required at 0200 for bridge duties.

0145   The Master comes to the bridge, acquaints himself with the situation on the chart, the OOW having fixed the position of the ship only five minutes before and then takes his customary position at the centre window. The OOW advises the Master of the present situation and again confirms that everything is running according to plan. The OOW continues his watch responsibilities as if the Master were not on the bridge.

0150   Master: 'Second Mate, I have the conn.'

       The OOW confirms the course and speed, advises the Master of any traffic that is of interest and logs the event.

       The Master is now in the situation that he will be giving the conning orders and the OOW monitoring and confirming these orders and advising the Master as appropriate.

0159   The OOW fixes the position of the ship.

       OOW: 'Captain, last fix shows ship on track. Planned reduction to manoeuvring full ahead at 0200.'

0200   Master: 'Confirmed' and rings the telegraph to reduce from full sea speed to manoeuvring full ahead.

       Standby seaman comes to bridge and steering gear is changed from automatic to manual and the wheel is manned. The helmsman moves the wheel and confirms that the steering is now under manual control.

0205   OOW: 'As planned I have now changed the fix period to 10 minutes and will be fixing using radar and visual.'

The OOW will now be spending more time at the chart, fixing more frequently and advising the Master of the progress of the ship, both relevant to the planned track and distance to run, speed and ETA at the pilot station. He will also be updating the parallel index on the appropriate radar so that the Master can acquaint himself with the situation. Both the OOW and the Master will be using the radars to monitor traffic.

0215 The OOW calls additional (previously warned) crew for pilot station and anchor standby duties in 30 minutes.

0220 OOW: 'Last fix shows vessel drifting slightly right of track. Suggest alter course to 035°T. Distance to run to pilot station 5 miles, suggest reduce speed to half ahead.'

Master acknowledges, corrects course and brings telegraph to half ahead.

0230 OOW: 'Fix confirms ship has regained track, suggest you steer 039°T.'

Master confirms and adjusts course as relevant.

OOW: 'We are on ETA, plan now requires speed of only 5 knots, suggest you reduce to slow ahead. Do you wish me to confirm pilot boarding.'

Master acknowledges and reduces to slow ahead.

Master: 'Yes, confirm ETA with pilot and ask his preferred boarding speed and which side he wants the lee.'

0235 OOW confirms pilot boarding on VHF and discusses boarding speed and pilot approach. He also despatches standby man/lookout to prepare the pilot ladder as appropriate and to advise relevant crewmembers to stand by forward and clear the anchors.

0240 Due to proximity of margins of safety fix time is now reduced to 6 minutes, parallel indexing still being used to confirm track maintenance. Speed is reduced to dead slow ahead, using the same procedures as before.

0245 Standby man returns and advises that the pilot ladder and ancillary gear is rigged as required.

The OOW advises engineroom of imminence of pilot boarding.

0250 OOW: 'Looks like the pilot vessel approaching. Do you want me to go down to meet the pilot.'

Master: 'Yes, but take a radio with you and keep me informed and get one of the anchor party to meet you there to haul the ladder back in.'

0252 The OOW fixes the ship's position and reminds the Master that the plan was that the engines would be stopped but speed would be kept at about four knots. The OOW leaves bridge to check the pilot boarding arrangements and to meet the pilot.

0256 Pilot boat alongside.

0257 Pilot on deck: the OOW advises the Master on the bridge via his radio that the pilot is aboard.

0300 Pilot on the bridge: the OOW confirms ship's position and safety and temporarily resumes the conn whilst the Master and pilot discuss the ship's particulars and the pilot's anticipated plan.

0305 Pilot takes conn and ship proceeds into the port area. The Master still has the responsibility for the safety of the ship and the OOW continues with his monitoring role as before.

The above scenario does not attempt to show how a ship's bridge will necessarily be organised. It does, however, show the large number of interactive events which may occur when a ship is in, what is to most seafarers, a relatively routine and straightforward situation.

The actual procedures exercised at the pilot boarding may vary considerably from ship to ship. Present requirements are that embarkation and disembarkation of a pilot should be supervised by a responsible officer of the ship.

In trying to comply with this, the personnel involved need to be aware that the Master will be alone on the bridge whilst the OOW is meeting the pilot or that another officer needs to be called specifically for this task. In the first instance the Master will make such a decision based upon the conditions at the time. It would be unwise to leave the bridge without an OOW in a situation such as heavy traffic, narrow margins of safety, strong tides or any combination of such factors, particularly as under such conditions the actual embarkation of the pilot could be delayed. Calling an additional officer may well be a better alternative, particularly if he has either just gone off watch or is required shortly. Whilst the final decision is at the discretion of the Master, the circumstances should have been allowed for and included at the planning stage.

In any circumstances where the Master has the conn, it is the duty of the OOW and any other personnel engaged in watchkeeping to provide the Master with sufficient information to enable him to make decisions appropriate to the situation. Most of these decisions will be based upon the original plan, but it is not solely the Master's duty to see that everything is going according to plan or otherwise. That duty is shared with the Master by the OOW who, by regularly fixing the ship's position, confirms that the original track is being maintained. It is also his duty to confirm that orders given by the Master, not just navigational orders, but all aspects of ship control, are carried out as required. Most importantly, it is for the OOW to advise the Master when he, the OOW, considers that things are not going according to plan or when a change of circumstances occurs.

DEBRIEF

Whenever possible after the successful completion of a passage the opportunity should be taken by the master to discuss the planning and execution of the passage with his team members. Possible weaknesses should be openly admitted so that they may be corrected or allowed for in future planned passages.

Such debrief need not take long and once the corrections to the plan have been made it can be saved for future use. In some instances—for example, where the ship frequently visits a certain port or regularly transits an area—it may be found advantageous to keep the charts and notebooks as they are. Unless major changes are made to the channels or navaids, etc., a planned passage will usually hold good for future visits, accepting that meteorological and tidal differences always have to be allowed for.

Some ships regularly trading to the same ports find it useful to have two sets of charts, one for the inward passage and one for the outward passage.

Passage plans can easily be held in a computer database, allowing for each extraction and correction when required. Shipowners and managers can use database-held planning to their advantage in that this system allows for simple standardisation throughout a fleet. Plans to the owners/managers own standards can be made and despatched to all of the company's ships, saving a duplication of effort and ensuring that the correct information and requirements are available. Computer access will then allow the plans to be easily modified in the light of the prevailing circumstances at very short notice.

Chapter 7

NAVIGATING WITH A PILOT ON BOARD

The relationship between the ship's team and an employed pilot is difficult to define.

The ship's Master is charged with the responsibility for the safety of the ship; pilots are engaged to assist with navigation in confined waters and to facilitate port approach, berthing and departure. The Master has the ultimate responsibility and has the right to take over from the pilot in the rare event of the pilot's inexperience or misjudgment. In practice, the Master may find himself in a position where he is not happy about the way the passage is being conducted by the pilot, yet is in no position to even query the pilot's actions as he, the Master, has no idea as to what should be happening.

Ideally, the Master and his team will be aware of the pilot's intentions and be in a position to be able to query his actions at any stage of the passage. This can only be brought about by:

1 The bridge team being aware of the difficulties and constraints of the pilotage area.

2 The pilot being aware of the characteristics and peculiarities of the ship.

3 The pilot being made familiar with the equipment at his disposal and aware of the degree of support he can expect from the ship's personnel.

Unfortunately this is not the way that things have developed. Boarding a strange ship, pilots often feel that they are unsupported. They know that the next part of the passage is going to be entirely up to themselves and consequently get on with and make the best of a bad job.

Equally, the OOW may feel that he is excluded from events. He doesn't know where the ship is going, how it is to get there, nor what is expected from him. Consequently, he is very likely to lose interest.

Such insecurities and doubts can quite easily be overcome by the ship's team operating a consistent system.

PLANNING

A well planned passage will not stop at the pilot boarding area. The planning will continue from sea to berth, or vice versa, the boarding of the pilot being part of the plan. The areas where the pilot actually has the conn will still have been planned by the navigator. This enables the Master and OOW to compare the progress of the ship with the planned track and also enables them to be aware of the constraints and other details of the passage. Abort and contingency planning will assist should the ship experience navigational or other problems.

MASTER/PILOT INFORMATION EXCHANGE

As stated above, the Master may not be aware of the area, the pilot unaware of the peculiarities of the ship. These problems can be minimised by establishing a routine Master/pilot exchange. When the pilot enters the bridge it is good practice for the Master to make time for a brief discussion with the pilot. The Master may need to delegate the conn to the OOW or other officer, as appropriate, in order to discuss the intended passage with the pilot. This will include such items as the pilot's planned route, his anticipated speeds and ETAs, both *en route* and at the destination, what assistance he expects from the shore, such as tugs and VTS information and what contingencies he may have in mind.

For his part, the Master needs to advise the pilot of the handling characteristics of his ship, in particular any unusual features and relevant information such as anchor condition, engine type and control and personnel availability. Much of this information can be readily available on a **Master/pilot exchange form**.

When these broad outlines have been established, the pilot will now need to be acquainted with the bridge, agreeing about how his instructions are to be executed (does he want to handle the controls or would he rather leave that to one of the ship's staff), where the VHF is situated and how to change channels and which radar is available for his use. In particular he needs to be advised of the present mode of the radar.

The pilot is now better placed to take the conn.

The above will obviously depend upon many factors.

1   The position of the pilot boarding area. Often this is such that there will be little time between the pilot actually entering the bridge and taking the conn.

2   The speed of the ship at the pilot boarding area. This too could limit time availability.

3   Environmental conditions such as poor visibility, strong winds, rough seas, strong tides or heavy traffic may inhibit the exchange.

If the exchange has not been carried out for any reason, even greater care will need to be exercised by the bridge team. This situation should be avoided if at all possible.

RESPONSIBILITY

Despite the presence of the pilot, the Master is still responsible for the safety of the ship. The pilot is the local expert and will obviously conduct the ship to the best of his ability, advising the Master as necessary and usually actually conducting the passage. This applies whether the pilotage is voluntary—i.e., the Master has requested assistance—or compulsory—i.e., the ship is required to take a local pilot within defined areas.

Frequently the Master will remain on the bridge during the pilotage. This obviously will depend on the circumstances. In the event of a long pilotage it would not be practicable for the Master to remain throughout. In this case he must remember to delegate his authority to a responsible officer, probably the OOW, exactly as he would at sea.

In any case the Master is in a poor position to question the pilot regarding the progress of the ship or its situation at any moment, unless he, the Master, knows what should be happening at that time.

MONITORING

The ship's progress needs to be monitored when the pilot has the conn exactly as it has to be under any other conditions. Such monitoring needs to be carried out by the OOW, and deviations from the planned track or speed observed and the Master made aware exactly as if he had the conn. From such information the Master will be in a position where he can question pilotage decisions with diplomacy and confidence.

Chapter 8

AUTOMATION OF BRIDGE SYSTEMS

The quest for safer means of navigation has existed since prehistoric times and reliability on ocean passages only became possible after the development of the sextant, chronometer and almanac.

In more recent times, satellite systems have provided an automatic read out accurate to about 100m, whilst the ships' systems have improved with more accurate gyro compasses, log systems and steering gear. The radar has been developed to provide true motion and automatic plotting. The presentation of the ship's position on an electronic chart is now possible.

At face value it might be expected that collisions and strandings were yesterday's problems, but the fact remains that their level of incidence remains significant.

The thesis of this book is not directed towards technology but towards people and the way people have to be prepared in advance in order to be able to evaluate the meaning of displays and printouts. Modern equipment is not error-prone or inaccurate—generally the performance standards are excellent—but if the operator fails to comprehend the significance of the information a potentially dangerous situation may develop.

Good seamanship must come first and must be part of all officers' training for it is that sense of awareness when things are going wrong and the expertise to remedy the situation upon which the navigator must depend.

HIGH-SPEED CRAFT

Most high-speed craft operate between two terminals a short distance apart; their main concern for safe navigation is collision avoidance and this is achieved directly from the radar. In restricted visibility and at night, to ensure safety, special night vision equipment is fitted and the radar is manned continuously whilst the pilot has an unrestricted view forward.

FERRIES

Ferries operate on regular routes where navigational control can assume a variety of methods. For example, on a cross-strait ferry, the navigation will usually be carried out on the radar screen on which is superimposed the key navigational features of the surrounding area, including traffic separation schemes and entry channels.

REGULAR TRADERS INCLUDING LINERS

Ships continually operating on a shuttle run clearly do not need to replan every voyage. Once the key elements of the navigational problem areas have been recognised, then taking into account weather and tidal information, satnav supported by radar parallel index may be sufficient to meet all the criteria of a well managed system. On some ships a 'reversible' track plotter works through a cassette tape, which can also be used as a 'recorder' if required subsequent to an incident.

OPEN MARKET TRADERS

In contrast to the liner services where the route planning can be prepared between fixed areas or particular destinations, those on board tramp ships have to be able to prepare a passage plan, often at short notice anywhere in the world. This places a considerable extra burden on the ship. It must, for example, carry a worldwide portfolio of charts and time must be made available to keep them up to date. Information about ports, services, pilotage, prevailing weather, tides, lights and radio aids need to be available. Ships and companies should be encouraged to maintain port files of their own so that draught restrictions and unusual features can be recorded.

PRECISION NAVIGATION Where it is essential to hold a ship within very narrow limits on a route which has many navigational hazards it is essential to control every aspect of the navigation. To do so vessels are fitted with accurate doppler logs to measure sideways motion, rate of turn indicators, automatic radius steering, computer generated predictors, path display overlay on the radar and operate constant radius turn manoeuvres.

ELECTRONIC CHARTS In future it can be envisaged that the paper chart will be displaced by a three-dimensional computer generated image through which the ship is navigated in accordance with a predetermined passage plan. Deviation from the track will no doubt sound an alarm and collision avoidance will be enhanced by advice from an expert system.

The evolution of modern electronic systems and their integration are likely to be proven first on ships operating on repetitive voyages and it will take a number of years until vessels navigating worldwide on 'the open market' will be provided with such comprehensive equipment.

Whatever systems are used, there is no substitute for training in good seamanship as this is the foundation upon which to build reliable performance.

This book has been designed to provide an insight into bridge organisation. Technical solutions to specific problems bring benefits, but it is people who plan ahead and ensure continuity over the entire watch system.

ABBREVIATIONS

BA ....British Admiralty

brg. ....Bearing

DR ....Dead Reckoning Position

DMA ....Defence Mapping Agency (USA)

dist....................................Distance

EOP ....End of Sea Passage

EP ....Estimated Position

ERBL.................................Electronic Range & Bearing Line

ETA ....Estimated Time of Arrival

GPS ....Global Positioning System

GMDSS.............................Global Maritime Distress and Safety System

HMSO ....Her Majesty's Stationery Office (UK)

ICS ....International Chamber of Shipping

IMO ....International Maritime Organization

Inmarsat ....International Maritime Satellite Organization

MF.....................................Medium Frequency

NLT ....Not Less Than

NMT ....Not More Than

OOW.................................Officer of the Watch

P/L....................................Position Line

PI ....Parallel Index

RDF...................................Radio Direction Finding

SAR...................................Search and Rescue

UMS ....Unattended Machinery Space

UKC..................................Underkeel Clearance

VHF...................................Very High Frequency Radio

VTS ....Vessel Traffic Services

GLOSSARY

AIR DRAUGHT
The height from the waterline to the highest point of the ship. This may be a masthead, but if crane jibs or derricks are raised could be significantly higher.

ABORT
The final point at which a ship can take action to avoid passing the point of no return.

CLEARING BEARING
The limiting bearing of a mark to one side of which the ship will be safe.

Defined by—not more than (NMT) or—not less than (NLT) a given bearing.

CONNING OFFICER
The person who has control of the ship. This may be the Master, the pilot or the OOW as appropriate.

COURSE TO STEER
The compass course steered to achieve a required track, allowing for set, leeway and compass error.

CURRENT
Non-tidal movement of the sea surface due mainly to meteorological, oceanographical or topographical causes.

DR POSITION
Dead reckoning—the position obtained from the resultant of the true course steered and the speed through the water.

EP POSITION
Estimated position—the position derived from the DR position adjusted for leeway and set and drift.

HEADING
The horizontal direction of the ship's head at a given moment measured in degrees clockwise from north. (This term does not necessarily require movement of the ship.)

LEEWAY
The angular effect on the ship's course caused by the prevailing wind. It is always downwind and varies according to the ship's speed, the wind speed, the ship's draught and freeboard and the relative direction of the wind.

PARALLEL INDEXING
A radar-based constant up-date of cross-track tendency.

POINT OF NO RETURN
The position after which the ship is committed to enter a constrained area.

RACON
Radar beacon which transmits when triggered by a ship's own radar transmission.

RANGE
See TRANSIT.

REPORTING POINT
A position where the ship is required to report to local harbour control.

SET AND DRIFT
The effect of the tidal stream and/or current on the ship's track. It is always downstream and varies according to the ship's speed and the relative direction and the strength of the stream.

SET—the direction that the stream runs towards
RATE—the speed of the stream
DRIFT—the resulting distance

(drift = rate x time)

Some ARPA manufacturers define drift as the speed of the stream.

SQUAT	The bodily sinkage of a ship in the water when making headway. Varying from ship to ship, it is often greater forward than aft and is more pronounced in shallow water.
TIDAL STREAM	The periodic horizontal movement of the sea surface caused by the gravitational forces of the sun and moon.
TIDAL WINDOW	The times between which, the tide having achieved a required height, it is safe for the ship to transit a certain area.
TRACK	The path followed, or to be followed, between one position and another.
TRACK MADE GOOD	The mean ground track actually achieved over a given period.
TRANSIT	Known in the US and Canada as a RANGE. When two objects are seen to be in line, they are said to be in transit.
UKC	Underkeel clearance. The vertical distance between the sea bed and the deepest part of the keel.
WAYPOINT	A reference point on the ship's planned track.
WHEEL-OVER POSITION	The point at which helm must be applied to achieve a required course alteration.

Please note that within this book the following terms are to be read as:

NAVIGATOR	The ship's officer tasked to produce the passage plan. He will also normally be responsible for all aspects of navigational equipment.
OFFICER OF THE WATCH (OOW)	The ship's officer responsible for the watch at a specific time.
WATCHKEEPER	An uncertificated crew member tasked with bridge watch-keeping duties.
HE/HIM	The masculine person is to include personnel of whatever gender.

Annex 1

IMO STCW Convention 1978
Regulation II/1

ANNEX A

BASIC PRINCIPLES TO BE OBSERVED IN KEEPING
A NAVIGATIONAL WATCH

1. Parties shall direct the attention of shipowners, ship operators, masters and watchkeeping personnel to the following principles which shall be observed to ensure that a safe navigational watch is maintained at all times.

2. The master of every ship is bound to ensure that watchkeeping arrangements are adequate for maintaining a safe navigational watch. Under the master's general direction, the officers of the watch are responsible for navigating the ship safely during their periods of duty when they will be particularly concerned with avoiding collision and stranding.

3. The basic principles, including but not limited to the following, shall be taken into account on all ships.

4. Watch arrangements

(a) The composition of the watch shall at all times be adequate and appropriate to the prevailing circumstances and conditions and shall take into account the need for maintaining a proper look-out.

(b) When deciding the composition of the watch on the bridge which may include appropriate deck ratings, the following factors, *inter alia*, shall be taken into account:

   (i) at no time shall the bridge be left unattended;

   (ii) weather conditions, visibility and whether there is daylight or darkness;

   (iii) proximity of navigational hazards which may make it necessary for the officer in charge of the watch to carry out additional navigational duties;

   (iv) use and operational condition of navigational aids such as radar or electronic position-indicating devices and any other equipment affecting the safe navigation of the ship;

   (v) whether the ship is fitted with automatic steering;

   (vi) any unusual demands on the navigational watch that may arise as a result of special operational circumstances.

5. Fitness for duty

The watch system shall be such that the efficiency of watchkeeping officers and watchkeeping ratings is not impaired by fatigue. Duties shall be so organized that the first watch at the commencement of a voyage and the subsequent relieving watches are sufficiently rested and otherwise fit for duty.

6. Navigation

(a) The intended voyage shall be planned in advance taking into consideration all pertinent information and any course laid down shall be checked before the voyage commences.

(b) During the watch the course steered, position and speed shall be checked at sufficiently frequent intervals, using any available navigational aids necessary, to ensure that the ship follows the planned course.

(c) The officer of the watch shall have full knowledge of the location and operation of all safety and navigational equipment on board the ship and shall be aware and take account of the operating limitations of such equipment.

(d) The officer in charge of a navigational watch shall not be assigned or undertake any duties which would interfere with the safe navigation of the ship.

7. Navigational equipment

(a) The officer of the watch shall make the most effective use of all navigational equipment at his disposal.

(b) When using radar, the officer of the watch shall bear in mind the necessity to comply at all times with the provisions on the use of radar contained in the applicable regulations for preventing collisions at sea.

(c) In cases of need the officer of the watch shall not hesitate to use the helm, engines and sound signalling apparatus.

8. Navigational duties and responsibilities

(a) The officer in charge of the watch shall:

(i) keep his watch on the bridge which he shall in no circumstances leave until properly relieved;

(ii) continue to be responsible for the safe navigation of the ship, despite the presence of the master on the bridge, until the master informs him specifically that he has assumed that responsibility and this is mutually understood;

(iii) notify the master when in any doubt as to what action to take in the interest of safety;

(iv) not hand over the watch to the relieving officer if he has reason to believe that the latter is obviously not capable of carrying out his duties effectively, in which case he shall notify the master accordingly.

(b) On taking over the watch the relieving officer shall satisfy himself as to the ship's estimated or true position and confirm its intended track, course and speed and shall note any dangers to navigation expected to be encountered during his watch.

(c) A proper record shall be kept of the movements and activities during the watch relating to the navigation of the ship.

9. Look-out

In addition to maintaining a proper look-out for the purpose of fully appraising the situation and the risk of collision, stranding and other dangers to navigation, the duties of the look-out shall include the detection of ships or aircraft in distress, shipwrecked persons, wrecks and debris. In maintaining a look-out the following shall be observed:

(a) the look-out must be able to give full attention to the keeping of a proper look-out and no other duties shall be undertaken or assigned which could interfere with that task;

(b) the duties of the look-out and helmsman are separate and the helmsman shall not be considered to be the look-out while steering, except in small ships where an unobstructed all-round view is provided at the steering position and there is no impairment of night vision or other impediment to the keeping of a proper look-out. The officer in charge of the watch may be the sole look-out in daylight provided that on each such occasion:

(i) the situation has been carefully assessed and it has been established without doubt that it is safe to do so;

(ii) full account has been taken of all relevant factors including, but not limited to:
—state of weather
—visibility
—traffic density
—proximity of danger to navigation
—the attention necessary when navigating in or near traffic separation schemes.

(iii) assistance is immediately available to be summoned to the bridge when any change in the situation so requires.

10. **Navigation with pilot embarked**

Despite the duties and obligations of a pilot, his presence on board does not relieve the master or officer in charge of the watch from their duties and obligations for the safety of the ship. The master and the pilot shall exchange information regarding navigation procedures, local conditions and the ship's characteristics. The master and officer of the watch shall co-operate closely with the pilot and maintain an accurate check of the ship's position and movement.

11. **Protection of the marine environment**

The master and officer in charge of the watch shall be aware of the serious effects of operational or accidental pollution of the marine environment and shall take all possible precautions to prevent such pollution, particularly within the framework of relevant international and port regulations.

ANNEX TO RESOLUTION 1

RECOMMENDATION ON OPERATIONAL GUIDANCE FOR OFFICERS IN CHARGE OF A NAVIGATIONAL WATCH

INTRODUCTION

1. This Recommendation contains operational guidance of general application for officers in charge of a navigational watch, which masters are expected to supplement as appropriate. It is essential that officers of the watch appreciate that the efficient performance of their duties is necessary in the interests of the safety of life and property at sea and the prevention of pollution of the marine environment.

GENERAL

2. The officer of the watch is the master's representative and his primary responsibility at all times is the safe navigation of the ship. He should at all times comply with the applicable regulations for preventing collisions at sea (see also paragraphs 22 and 23).

3. It is of special importance that at all times the officer of the watch ensures that an efficient look-out is maintained. In a ship with a separate chart room the officer of the watch may visit the chart room, when essential, for a short period for the necessary performance of his navigational duties, but he should previously satisfy himself that it is safe to do so and ensure that an efficient lookout is maintained.

4. The officer of the watch should bear in mind that the engines are at his disposal and he should not hesitate to use them in case of need. However, timely notice of intended variations of engine speed should be given where possible. He should also know the handling characteristics of his ship, including its stopping distance, and should appreciate that other ships may have different handling characteristics.

5. The officer of the watch should also bear in mind that the sound signalling apparatus is at his disposal and he should not hesitate to use it in accordance with the applicable regulations for preventing collisions at sea.

TAKING OVER THE NAVIGATIONAL WATCH

6. The relieving officer of the watch should ensure that members of his watch are fully capable of performing their duties, particularly as regards their adjustment to night vision.

7. The relieving officer of the watch should not take over the watch until his vision is fully adjusted to the light conditions and he has personally satisfied himself regarding:

(a) standing orders and other special instructions of the master relating to navigation of the ship;

(b) position, course, speed and draught of the ship;

(c) prevailing and predicted tides, currents, weather, visibility and the effect of these factors upon course and speed;

(d) navigational situation, including but not limited to the following:

(i) operational condition of all navigational and safety equipment being used or likely to be used during the watch;

(ii) errors of gyro and magnetic compasses;

(iii) presence and movement of ships in sight or known to be in the vicinity;

(iv) conditions and hazards likely to be encountered during his watch;

(v) possible effects of heel, trim, water density and squat* on underkeel clearance.

8. If at the time the officer of the watch is to be relieved a manoeuvre or other action to avoid any hazard is taking place, the relief of the officer should be deferred until such action has been completed.

PERIODIC CHECKS OF NAVIGATIONAL EQUIPMENT

9. Operational tests of shipboard navigational equipment should be carried out at sea as frequently as practicable and as circumstances permit, in particular when hazardous conditions affecting navigation are expected; where appropriate these tests should be recorded.

10. The officer of the watch should make regular checks to ensure that:

(a) the helmsman or the automatic pilot is steering the correct course;

(b) the standard compass error is determined at least once a watch and, when possible, after any major alteration of course; the standard and gyro-compasses are frequently compared and repeaters are synchronized with their master compass;

(c) the automatic pilot is tested manually at least once a watch.

(d) the navigation and signal lights and other navigational equipment are functioning properly.

AUTOMATIC PILOT

11. The officer of the watch should bear in mind the necessity to comply at all times with the requirements of Regulation 19, Chapter V of the International Convention for the Safety of Life at Sea, 1974. He should take into account the need to station the helmsman and to put the steering into manual control in good time to allow any potentially hazardous situation to be dealt with in a safe manner. With a ship under automatic steering it is highly dangerous to allow a situation to develop to the point where the officer of the watch is without assistance and has to break the continuity of the look-out in order to take emergency action. The change-over from automatic to manual steering and vice-versa should be made by, or under the supervision of, a responsible officer.

ELECTRONIC NAVIGATIONAL AIDS

12. The officer of the watch should be thoroughly familiar with the use of electronic navigational aids carried, including their capabilities and limitations.

13. The echo-sounder is a valuable navigational aid and should be used whenever appropriate.

RADAR

14. The officer of the watch should use the radar when appropriate and whenever restricted visibility is encountered or expected, and at all times in congested waters having due regard to its limitations.

15. Whenever radar is in use, the officer of the watch should select an appropriate range scale, observe the display carefully and plot effectively.

16. The officer of the watch should ensure that range scales employed are changed at sufficiently frequent intervals so that echoes are detected as early as possible.

17. It should be borne in mind that small or poor echoes may escape detection.

---

* Squat: The decrease in clearance beneath the ship which occurs when the ship moves through the water and is caused both by bodily sinkage and by change of trim. The effect is accentuated in shallow water and is reduced with a reduction in ship's speed.

18. The officer of the watch should ensure that plotting or systematic analysis is commenced in ample time.

19. In clear weather, whenever possible, the officer of the watch should carry out radar practice.

NAVIGATION IN COASTAL WATERS

20. The largest scale chart on board, suitable for the area and corrected with the latest available information, should be used. Fixes should be taken at frequent intervals; whenever circumstances allow, fixing should be carried out by more than one method.

21. The officer of the watch should positively identify all relevant navigation marks.

CLEAR WEATHER

22. The officer of the watch should take frequent and accurate compass bearings of approaching ships as a means of early detection of risk of collision; such risk may sometimes exist even when an appreciable bearing change is evident, particularly when approaching a very large ship or a tow or when approaching a ship at close range. He should also take early and positive action in compliance with the applicable regulations for preventing collisions at sea and subsequently check that such action is having the desired effect.

RESTRICTED VISIBILITY

23. When restricted visibility is encountered or expected, the first responsibility of the officer of the watch is to comply with the relevant rules of the applicable regulations for preventing collisions at sea, with particular regard to the sounding of fog signals, proceeding at a safe speed and having the engines ready for immediate manoeuvres. In addition, he should;

    (a) inform the master (see paragraph 24);

    (b) post a proper look-out and helmsman and, in congested waters, revert to hand steering immediately;

    (c) exhibit navigation lights;

    (d) operate and use the radar.

It is important that the officer of the watch should know the handling characteristics of his ship, including its stopping distance, and should appreciate that other ships may have different handling characteristics.

CALLING THE MASTER

24. The officer of the watch should notify the master immediately in the following circumstances;

    (a) if restricted visibility is encountered or expected;

    (b) if the traffic conditions or the movements of other ships are causing concern;

    (c) if difficulty is experienced in maintaining course;

    (d) on failure to sight land, a navigation mark or to obtain soundings by the expected time;

    (e) if, unexpectedly, land or a navigation mark is sighted or change in soundings occurs;

    (f) on the breakdown of the engines, steering gear or any essential navigational equipment;

    (g) in heavy weather if in any doubt about the possibility of weather damage;

    (h) if the ship meets any hazard to navigation, such as ice or derelicts;

(i) in any other emergency or situation in which he is in any doubt.

Despite the requirement to notify the master immediately in the foregoing circumstances, the officer of the watch should in addition not hesitate to take immediate action for the safety of the ship, where circumstances so require.

NAVIGATION WITH PILOT EMBARKED

25. If the officer of the watch is in any doubt as to the pilot's actions or intentions, he should seek clarification from the pilot; if doubt still exists, he should notify the master immediately and take whatever action is necessary before the master arrives.

WATCHKEEPING PERSONNEL

26. The officer of the watch should give watchkeeping personnel all appropriate instructions and information which will ensure the keeping of a safe watch including an appropriate look-out.

SHIP AT ANCHOR

27. If the master considers it necessary, a continuous navigational watch should be maintained at anchor. In all circumstances, while at anchor, the officer of the watch should:

(a) determine and plot the ship's position on the appropriate chart as soon as practicable; when circumstances permit, check at sufficiently frequent intervals whether the ship is remaining securely at anchor by taking bearings of fixed navigation marks or readily identifiable shore objects;

(b) ensure that an efficient look-out is maintained;

(c) ensure that inspection rounds of the ship are made periodically;

(d) observe meteorological and tidal conditions and the state of the sea;

(e) notify the master and undertake all necessary measures if the ship drags anchor;

(f) ensure that the state of readiness of the main engines and other machinery is in accordance with the master's instructions;

(g) if visibility deteriorates, notify the master and comply with the applicable regulations for preventing collisions at sea;

(h) ensure that the ship exhibits the appropriate lights and shapes and that appropriate sound singals are made at all times, as required;

(i) take measures to protect the environment from pollution by the ship and comply with applicable pollution regulations.

UPKEEP OF THE CHART OUTFIT

Chart outfit management

Extract from *The Mariner's Handbook*, reproduced with the permission of
the Hydrographer of the Navy

Chart outfits

An Outfit of Charts, in addition to the necessary Standard Admiralty Folios, or selected charts made up into folios as required, should include the following publications.

Chart Correction Log and Folio Index
Admiralty Notices to Mariners, Weekly Editions, subsequent to the last *Annual Summary of Admiralty Notices to Mariners*. Earlier ones may be required to correct a volume of *Admiralty List of Lights* approaching its re-publication date, see 1.111.
Chart 5011—Symbols and Abbreviations used on Admiralty Charts.
Appropriate volumes of:
  Admiralty Sailing Directions;
  Admiralty List of Lights;
  Admiralty List of Radio Signals;
  Admiralty Tide Tables;
  Tidal Stream Atlases;
  The Mariner's Handbook.

The supplier of the outfit will state the number of the last Notice to Mariners to which it has been corrected.

Chart management system

A system is required to keep an outfit of charts up-to-date. It should include arrangements for the supply of New Charts. New Editions of charts and extra charts, as well as new editions and supplements of *Admiralty Sailing Directions* and other nautical publications, if necessary at short notice.

On notification by *Admiralty Notice to Mariners* that a new edition of one of the books, or a new Supplement to one, has been published, it should be obtained as soon as possible. Corrections to a book subsequent to such a Notice will refer to the new edition or to the book as corrected by the Supplement.

Arrangements should be made for the continuous receipt of Radio Navigational Warnings, *Admiralty Notices to Mariners*, and notices affecting any foreign charts carried.

A system of documentation is required which shows quickly and clearly that all relevant corrections have been received and applied, and that New Charts, New Editions and the latest editions of publications and their supplements have been obtained or ordered.

Method. For users of Standard Admiralty Folios of charts, the following is a convenient method to manage a chart outfit. Where only a selection of the charts in the Standard Admiralty Folios are held, the method can be readily adapted.

Chart Correction Log and Folio Index (NP 133a) is suitable. It contains sheets providing a numerical index of charts, indicates in which folio they are held, and has space against each chart for logging Notices to Mariners affecting it.

It is divided into three parts:

Part I   Navigational Charts (including Decca, Omega and Loran-C).
Part II   Admiralty reproductions of Australian and New Zealand charts.
Part III   Miscellaneous Charts.

At the beginning of Part I are sheets for recording the publication of New Charts and New Editions, and instructions for the use of the Log.

On receiving a chart outfit

Charts. Enter the number of the Notice to which the outfit has been corrected in the Chart Correction Log. Insert the Folio Number on the thumb-label of each chart. If not using Standard Admiralty Folios, enter the Folio Number against each chart of the Log.

Consult the Index of Charts Affected in the Weekly Edition of Notices to Mariners containing the last Notice to which the outfit has been corrected, and all subsequent Weekly Editions. If any charts held are mentioned, enter the numbers of the Notices affecting them against the charts concerned in the Log, and then correct the charts.

Consult the latest monthly Notice listing Temporary and Preliminary Notices in force, and the Temporary and Preliminary Notices in each Weekly Edition subsequent to it. If any charts are affected by those Notices, enter in pencil the numbers of the Notices against the charts in the Log, and then correct the charts for them (also in pencil).

Extract all Temporary and Preliminary Notices from Weekly Editions subsequent to the current *Annual Summary of Admiralty Notices to Mariners* and make them into a 'Temporary and Preliminary Notices' file.

Radio Navigational Warnings. From all Weekly Editions of the current year, detach Section III and file, or list the messages by their areas. Determine which messages are still in force from the Weekly Edition issued monthly, which lists them. Insert the information from these messages on any relevant charts.

Sailing Directions. From Weekly Editions subsequent to the current *Annual Summary of Admiralty Notices to Mariners*, detach Section IV and file.

Admiralty List of Lights. From Weekly Editions subsequent to those supplied with the volumes, detach Section V and insert all corrections in the volumes.

Admiralty List of Radio Signals. From Weekly Editions subsequent to those announcing publication of the volumes, detach section VI and insert all corrections in the volumes.

Admiralty Tide Tables. From *Annual Summary of Admiralty Notices to Mariners* for the year in progress, insert any corrigenda to the volume.

Chart 5011—Symbols and Abbreviations used on Admiralty Charts. Use any Notices supplied with the pamphlet to correct it.

On notification of the publication of a New Chart or New Edition

When a New Chart or New Edition is published, this is announced by a Notice giving the Date of Publication and the numbers of any Temporary and Preliminary Notices affecting it. From such Notices, enter on the appropriate page of Part I of the Log:

- Number of the Chart;

- Date of Publication;

- Number of the Notice announcing publication;

- Numbers of any Temporary and Preliminary Notices affecting the chart (in pencil).

Until the chart is received, the numbers of any subsequent Permanent, Temporary or Preliminary Notices affecting it should be recorded with the above entry.

On receiving a New Chart or New Edition

Enter the following details in the Log.

- If a New Chart, the Folio Number against the Chart Number in the Index.

- On the sheet at the beginning of Part I, the date of receipt of the chart.

- Against the Chart Number in the Notices to Mariners column of the Index Sheet, 'NC' or 'NE' with the date of publication, followed by a double vertical line to close the space.

- In the Notices to Mariners column of the chart in the Index, the numbers of any Notices recorded against the chart on the sheet at the beginning of Part I.

Enter the Folio Number on the thumb-label of the chart. Correct the chart for any Notices transferred from Part I as described above, and for any Radio Navigational Warnings affecting it. Destroy any superseded chart.

On receiving a chart additional to the outfit

Enter the Folio Number on the thumb-label of the chart. If not using Standard Admiralty Folios, enter the Folio Number against the chart in the Index of the Log.

Enter the number of the last Notice to which the chart has been corrected against the chart in the Index of the Log.

Consult the Index of Charts Affected in each Weekly Edition of *Admiralty Notices to Mariners* from the one including the last Small Correction entered on the chart. If any Notices affecting the chart have been issued since the last Notice for which it has been corrected, enter them against the chart in the Log and correct the chart for them.

Consult the file of Temporary and Preliminary Notices. If any Notices affect the chart, enter their numbers against the chart in the Log, and correct the chart for them.

From the file or list of Radio Navigational Warnings, see if any Warnings affect the chart. If so, annotate the chart accordingly.

On receiving a replacement chart

Insert the Folio Number on the thumb-label of the chart.

From the record kept in the Log, correct the replacement chart for any Notices affecting it published after the last Notice entered on it under Small Corrections.

Consult the file of Temporary and Preliminary Notices, enter any affecting the chart in the Log, and correct the chart if relevant.

Consult the file or list of Radio Navigational Warnings. If any of the Warnings affect the chart and are required on it, annotate it accordingly.

On receiving a Weekly Edition of Admiralty Notices to Mariners

Check that the serial number of the Weekly Edition is in sequence with Editions already received, then:

From the Index of Charts Affected, enter in the Log the numbers of the Notices affecting the charts held.

Turn to the end of Section II to see if any Temporary or Preliminary Notices have been published or cancelled. If they have been, add to or amend the entries in the Log against the charts accordingly.

Examine the 'Admiralty Publications' Notice to see if any relevant New Charts or New Editions have been published, or charts withdrawn. If they have, take action.

Detach and use Sections III to VI as follows:

Section III. Check printed text of messages against any signalled versions. File Section, or note down messages by their areas, and bring up-to-date previous information on the file and any notations made on charts;

Section IV: Add to file or list;

Section V: Cut up and use to correct *Admiralty List of Lights*;

Section VI: Cut up and use to correct *Admiralty List of Radio Signals*;

Resecure chart correcting blocks to Section II.

From folios affected, extract and correct charts for the appropriate Notices in Section II.

Correction of charts

General information

No correction, except those given in Section II of *Admiralty Notices to Mariners*, Weekly Editions, should be made to any chart in ink.

Corrections to charts from information received from authorities other than the Hydrographic Department may be noted in pencil, but no charted danger should be expunged without the authority of the Hydrographer of the Navy.

All corrections given in Notices to Mariners should be inserted on the charts affected. When they have been completed the numbers of the Notices should be entered clearly and neatly; permanent Notices in waterproof violet ink, Temporary and Preliminary Notices in pencil.

Temporary and Preliminary Notices should be rubbed out as soon as the Notice is received cancelling them.

Chart 5011—Symbols and Abbreviations used on Admiralty Charts should be followed to ensure uniformity of corrections. These symbols are invariably indicated on Overlay Correction Tracings.

If several charts are affected by one Notice, the largest scale chart should be corrected first to appreciate the detail of the correction.

Last correction

When correcting a chart; first check that the last published correction to it, which is given at the end of the new Notice, has been made to the chart.

Detail required

The amount of detail shown on a chart varies with the scale of the chart. On a large scale chart, for example, full details of all lights and fog signals are shown, but on smaller scales the order of reduction of information is Elevation, Period, Range, until on an ocean chart of the area only lights with a range of 15 miles or more will normally be inserted, and then only their light-star and magenta flare. On the other hand, radio beacons are omitted from large scale charts where their use would be inappropriate, and, unless they are long range beacons, from ocean charts.

Notices adding detail to charts indicate how much detail should be added to each chart, but Notices deleting detail do not always make this distinction. If a shortened description would result in ambiguity between adjacent aids, detail should be retained. The insertion of excessive detail not only clutters the chart, but can lead to errors, since the charts quoted as affected in each Notice assume the Mariner has reduced with the scale of the charts the details inserted by previous Notices.

Alterations

Erasures should never be made. Where necessary, detail should be crossed through, or in the case of lines, such as depth contours or limits, crossed with a series of short double strokes, slanting across the line. Typing correction fluids, such as 'Tipp-Ex', should not be used.

Alterations to depth contours, deletion of depths to make way for detail, etc, are not mentioned in Notices unless they have some navigational significance.

Where tinted depths contours require amendment, the line should be amended, but the tint, which is only intended to draw attention to the line, can usually remain untouched. Where information is displaced for clarity, its proper position should be indicated by a small circle and arrow.

Blocks

Some Notices are accompanied by reproductions of portions of charts (known as 'Blocks'). When correcting charts from blocks, the following points should be borne in mind.

- A block may not only indicate the insertion of new information, but also the omission of matter previously shown. The text of the Notice should invariably be read carefully.

- The limiting lines of a block are determined for convenience of reproduction. They need not be strictly adhered to when cutting out for pasting on the chart, provided that the preceding paragraph is taken into consideration.

- Owing to distortion the blocks do not always fit the chart exactly. When pasting a block on a chart, therefore, care should be taken that the more important navigational features fit as closely as possible. This is best done by fitting the block while it is dry and making two or three pencil ticks round the edges for use as fitting marks after the paste is applied to the chart.

Completion of corrections

Whenever a correction has been made to a chart the number of the Notice and the year (if not already shown) should be entered in the bottom left-hand corner of the chart: the entries for permanent Notices as Small Corrections, and those for Temporary and Preliminary Notices, in pencil, below the line of Small Corrections.

NB This example covers UK Admiralty charts. Appropriate guidance from other charting authorities should be studied for their chart correcting system.

INDEX

NOTES

NOTES

NOTES

THE NAUTICAL INSTITUTE
ON
BRIDGE OPERATIONS

THE following books, videos and briefings may be purchased separately or together.

BOOK

BRIDGE TEAM MANAGEMENT is produced in conjunction with the Nautical Institute and whilst it can be used on its own, is part of a package which includes a series of Video cassettes produced by Videotel, London, accompanied by distance learning booklets.

VIDEOS

The Nautical Institute is supporting the production of three training videos which are being made by Videotel Marine International.

BRIDGE WATCHKEEPING PROCEDURES: This video is designed to reinforce good bridge watchkeeping practices.

PASSAGE PLANNING: This video is designed to demonstrate the need to prepare passages in advance, berth to berth, with the overall objective of giving the watchkeeping officer a plan to follow and sufficient information to enable him to do that easily.

THE MASTER/PILOT RELATIONSHIP: This video recognises that the master and pilot are two professionals with a common purpose. It discusses responsibilities, the exchange of information and ways of ensuring the best basis for a safe passage through busy confined and sometimes hazardous waters.

Information concerning these three videos can be obtained directly from Videotel Productions, Ramilles House, 1-2 Ramilles Street, London W1V 1DF, UK: Tel: 071-439 6301.

ON-BOARD TRAINING MANUAL

BRIDGE WATCHKEEPING: This is a training manual with a difference. It is written in open learning format with principles and practices well illustrated with diagrams. It is produced for the guidance of junior watchkeeping officers and trainees.

OBJECTIVES

On completion of the study programme contained in the book the junior officer should have a better understanding of:

A The stages of the passage and the structure of the bridge watchkeeping organisation.
B The watchkeeping tasks of the bridge officer.
C The role of the bridge equipment.
D The professional relationship between the master and the bridge watchkeeping officers.

CONTENTS

1. Introduction to bridge watchkeeping procedures.
2. The stages of the passage.
3. Preparing for sea.
4. Alongside the berth/at anchor.
5. Embarking the pilot/updating the plan.
6. Undocking/weighing anchor.
7. Narrow Waters.
8. Disembarking the pilot.
9. Coastal waters.
10. Ocean areas
11. Making a landfall/preparing for arrival/docking.
12. Professional relationship between master and bridge watchkeeping officer.

This book draws upon existing regulations and codes as the basis of the text. It is being written by **Captain H.H. Francis, MNI,** and **Captain T.C. Rooney, BSc, FNI,** and verified by the Isle of Man Branch.

If you would like more information about these publications please write or fax to **Mrs J. E. Miller, Publications Officer (Fax 071 401 2537), The Nautical Institute, 202 Lambeth Road, London SE1 7LQ, UK.**

- -

THE NAUTICAL INSTITUTE

The Nautical Institute is an international professional body for qualified mariners whose primary aim is to promote high standards of knowledge, competence and qualification amongst those in control of seagoing craft. There are some 6,200 members in seventy different countries who comprise seagoing deck officers, masters, pilots, naval officers, harbour masters, nautical surveyors, superintendents, fleet managers, lecturers, and others with nautical qualifications working in the shipping industry and armed services.

Full membership is linked to the standard of an approved master mariner's certificate and naval command qualifications—The Institute publishes a monthly journal called SEAWAYS.